HEATH
MIDDLE LEVEL
LITERATURE

Future Directions

Individuals can help shape Earth's future. What can you learn
from the world of science fiction? How can your reading
help you be more aware of the need to
preserve the environment?

AUTHORS

Donna Alvermann
Linda Miller Cleary
Kenneth Donelson
Donald Gallo
Alice Haskins
J. Howard Johnston
John Lounsbury
Alleen Pace Nilsen
Robert Pavlik
Jewell Parker Rhodes
Alberto Alvaro Ríos
Sandra Schurr
Lyndon Searfoss
Julia Thomason
Max Thompson
Carl Zon

D.C. Heath and Company
Lexington, Massachusetts / Toronto, Ontario
HEATH

STAFF CREDITS

EDITORIAL Barbara A. Brennan, Susan Belt Cogley, DeVona Dors, Christopher Johnson, Rita M. Sullivan, Patricia B. Weiler
Proofreading: JoAnne B. Sgroi

CONTRIBUTING WRITERS Kathy Tuchman Glass, Jo Pitkin

SERIES DESIGN Robin Herr

BOOK DESIGN Caroline Bowden, Daniel Derdula, Susan Geer, Diana Maloney, Angela Sciaraffa, Bonnie Chayes Yousefian
Art Editing: Carolyn Langley

PHOTOGRAPHY *Series Photography Coordinator:* Carmen Johnson
Photo Research Supervisor: Martha Friedman
Photo Researchers: Wendy Enright, Po-yee McKenna, PhotoSearch, Inc., Gillian Speeth, Denise Theodores
Assignment Photography Coordinators: Susan Doheny, Gayna Hoffman, Shawna Johnston

COMPUTER PREPRESS Ricki Pappo, Kathy Meisl
Richard Curran, Michele Locatelli

PERMISSIONS Dorothy B. McLeod

PRODUCTION Patrick Connolly

Cover Photographs: © William Lesch, SWANSTOCK; inset of Earth: courtesy NASA.
Cover Design: Midnight Oil Studios

Published simultaneously in Canada

Printed in the United States of America

International Standard Book Number: 0-669-32114-1
1 2 3 4 5 6 7 8 9 10-RRD-99 98 97 96 95 94

Middle Level Authors

Donna Alvermann, University of Georgia
Alice Haskins, Howard County Public Schools, Maryland
J. Howard Johnston, University of South Florida
John Lounsbury, Georgia College
Sandra Schurr, University of South Florida
Julia Thomason, Appalachian State University
Max Thompson, Appalachian State University
Carl Zon, California Assessment Collaborative

Literature and Language Arts Authors

Linda Miller Cleary, University of Minnesota
Kenneth Donelson, Arizona State University
Donald Gallo, Central Connecticut State University
Alleen Pace Nilsen, Arizona State University
Robert Pavlik, Cardinal Stritch College, Milwaukee
Jewell Parker Rhodes, California State University, Northridge
Alberto Alvaro Ríos, Arizona State University
Lyndon Searfoss, Arizona State University

Teacher Consultants

Suzanne Aubin, Patapsco Middle School, Ellicott City, Maryland
Judy Baxter, Newport News Public Schools, Newport News, Virginia
Saundra Bryn, Director of Research and Development, El Mirage, Arizona
Lorraine Gerhart, Elmbrook Middle School, Elm Grove, Wisconsin
Kathy Tuchman Glass, Burlingame Intermediate School, Burlingame, California
Lucretia Pannozzo, John Jay Middle School, Katonah, New York
Carol Schultz, Jerling Junior High, Orland Park, Illinois
Jeanne Siebenman, Grand Canyon University, Phoenix, Arizona
Gail Thompson, Garey High School, Pomona, California
Rufus Thompson, Grace Yokley School, Ontario, California
Tom Tufts, Conniston Middle School, West Palm Beach, Florida
Edna Turner, Harpers Choice Middle School, Columbia, Maryland
C. Anne Webb, Buerkle Junior High School, St. Louis, Missouri
Geri Yaccino, Thompson Junior High School, St. Charles, Illinois

CONTENTS

TIME TRAVEL   8-9

What might you need one hundred years from now?

ASKING BIG QUESTIONS ABOUT THE THEME   10-11

What will life be like in the twenty-first century?

What decisions being made today will affect Earth?

What will be the future consequences of today's decisions?

How can individuals help shape the future?

THE LITERATURE

RAY BRADBURY   **The Naming of Names   12-29**
SHORT STORY

Who are the true Martians? Take a trip to Mars and find out.

Traditional Navajo   **Song of the Earth Spirit   30-31**
POEM

Why is it important to love and cherish the earth?

ELIZABETH VITTON — **Paradise Lost**   32-39

NONFICTION

*People have the power to save or destroy the rain forests.
Which will it be?*

KURT VONNEGUT, JR. — **Harrison Bergeron**   40-51

SHORT STORY

Does this story have the answer to equality?

MAY SWENSON — **Orbiter 5 Shows How Earth Looks from the
Moon**   52-53

POEM

*People see unusual shapes and outlines in the moon and
clouds. What imaginative outlines does this poet see
in Earth?*

ARTHUR C. CLARKE — **If I Forget Thee,
Oh Earth . . .
54-61**

SHORT STORY

*Exiles from Earth
look with longing
at their
abandoned
planet. Will
Earth ever recover?*

STEPHEN DAVID — **Homecoming**   62-77

SHORT STORY

*The plan is to return to Earth, but some people want to
stay where they are. Are they wise?*

MICHAEL RYAN

So, You Want to Be an Astronaut
78-83
NONFICTION

Planning for life aboard space ships involves a grueling interview process, among other challenges.

T. ERNESTO
BETHANCOURT

User Friendly 84-99
SHORT STORY

Kevin is taken by surprise when his computer takes on human qualities. What will his new friend do in the name of friendship?

RICHARD RIVE

Where the Rainbow Ends 100-101
POEM

Will human beings ever find the end of the rainbow?

ASKING BIG QUESTIONS ABOUT THE LITERATURE

What will life be like in the twenty-first century? 102

What decisions being made today will affect Earth? 103

What will be the future consequences of today's decisions? 104

How can individuals help shape the future? 105

P R O J E C T S

1 WRITING WORKSHOP
THE ART OF PERSUASION 106-111
Take a stand about a local or national problem you feel passionate about.

2 COOPERATIVE LEARNING
PRODUCING A NEWSCAST 112-113
Produce a newscast for a futuristic television station reporting the current news.

3 HELPING YOUR COMMUNITY
TAKING ACTION 114-115
Examine a community problem and take some action to help improve the situation.

PUTTING IT ALL TOGETHER 116-117
What have you learned about future directions?

LITERARY ELEMENTS: Setting and Imagery 118-119

GLOSSARY OF LITERARY TERMS 120-124

ACKNOWLEDGMENTS AND CREDITS 125

FULL PRONUNCIATION KEY FOR FOOTNOTED WORDS 126

TIME TRAVEL

What will life be like in future centuries? Pretend that your class has built a time machine, and you've decided to go forward to a place 100 years from now. Where will you go? What will you take with you into this future time?

1 Planning a Time Trip

In a small group, brainstorm for a list of places and then decide where you'll go. Then decide what objects you want to take with you to this future time. Will you take a birth certificate, photos of your family, a notebook, favorite books, or a toothbrush? Now think of ideas and concepts you'd like to share with the future. Will the people you meet know about freedom of speech or kindness to others? Avoid choosing any objects, ideas, or concepts that might cause physical or emotional harm to future life. Make a chart of your choices like the one on this page. Add the choices of everyone in your group. When you complete your chart, narrow the items down to five objects, ideas, and concepts. Circle them on the chart.

Objects	Ideas	Concepts
CD player	carless society	freedom of speech
dental floss		

Defend Your Choices

Now that your group has decided where to go and what to take, have a class discussion. Appoint a spokesperson for your group who will tell the class where your group chooses to go, what the group plans to take, and why. Try to persuade the other groups that your choices are right. Prepare to defend each of your choices by discussing with your group how each choice will be useful and beneficial in 100 years.

A Class Decision

Listen carefully as each group reports to the class on the essential objects, ideas, and concepts that might be needed in the future. Then take a vote among your classmates to decide which five would be the most useful and beneficial for people in 100 years. Make a class chart to post on the bulletin board. Pack up the time machine and let it take each group where it wants to go.

Asking Big Questions About the Theme

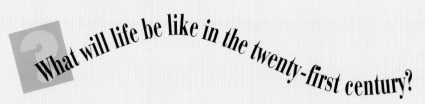

What will life be like in the twenty-first century?

Pretend you're a member of an architectural design firm of the twenty-first century. Join a small group and divide the following futuristic places among the members: the outside of a house or apartment, buildings in the center of a city or town, a community park. Draw or sketch what the place you select might look like. Then arrange your drawing on a poster with the drawings of your group members.

What decisions being made today will affect Earth?

Individually or in groups, go through a newspaper or magazine and circle articles that relate to some decision that will have an impact on people or society in 100 years. For example, look for an article dealing with medicine or industry. In your journal, make a list of these decisions that will affect Earth.

> Cars—
> non-polluting
> electric
> self-cleaning
>
> Medicine—
> from plants
> accessible to all

What will be the future consequences of today's decisions?

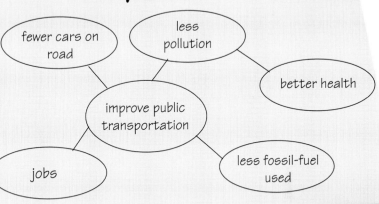

Think about decisions being made today in the fields of health, science, the arts, or even decisions you make about your own life. Choose one decision and write it in the center of a web or cluster. Then add consequences of the decision in circles joined to the cluster or web, as in the example on this page.

(Web diagram:)
- improve public transportation
  - fewer cars on road
  - less pollution
    - better health
  - jobs
  - less fossil-fuel used

How can individuals help shape the future?

Brainstorm with a partner to find a problem in your community that needs solving, such as the need for recycling or the need for preserving wet lands. Then, on your own, jot down ideas in your journal about what you can do to help solve this problem. Finally discuss your decisions with your partner and present your ideas to the class.

NOW Think!

What is the biggest challenge facing you in the future? How would you solve it? As you read the literature in this unit, compare your ideas about future challenges and solutions with those of characters in the selections. Do you find good solutions in the selections?

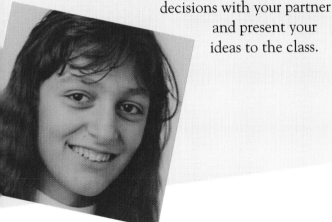

THE NAMING OF NAMES

RAY BRADBURY

The rocket metal cooled in the meadow winds. Its lid gave a bulging *pop*. From its clock interior stepped a man, a woman, and three children. The other passengers whispered away across the Martian meadow, leaving the man alone among his family.

The man felt his hair flutter and the tissues of his body draw tight as if he were standing at the center of a vacuum. His wife, before him, seemed almost to whirl away in smoke. The children, small seeds, might at any instant be sown to all the Martian climes.[1]

The children looked up at him, as people look to the sun to tell what time of their life it is. His face was cold.

"What's wrong?" asked his wife.

"Let's get back on the rocket."

"Go back to Earth?"

"Yes! Listen!"

The wind blew as if to flake away their identities. At any moment the Martian air might draw his soul from him, as marrow[2] comes from a white bone. He felt submerged in a chemical that could dissolve his intellect and burn away his past.

1. **climes:** countries or regions.
2. **marrow** [mar′ ō]: soft tissue in bones.

The Naming of Names

They looked at Martian hills that time had worn with a crushing pressure of years. They saw the old cities, lost in their meadows, lying like children's delicate bones among the blowing lakes of grass.

"Chin up, Harry," said his wife. "It's too late. We've come over sixty million miles."

The children with their yellow hair hollered at the deep dome of Martian sky. There was no answer but the racing hiss of wind through the stiff grass.

He picked up the luggage in his cold hands. "Here we go," he said__a man standing on the edge of a sea, ready to wade in and be drowned.

They walked into town.

Their name was Bittering— Harry and his wife Cora, Dan, Laura, and David. They built a small white cottage and ate good breakfasts there, but the fear was never gone. It lay with Mr. Bittering and Mrs. Bittering, a third unbidden partner at every midnight talk, at every dawn awakening.

"I feel like a salt crystal," he said, "in a mountain stream, being washed away. We don't belong here. We're Earth people. This is Mars. It was meant for Martians. For heaven's sake, Cora, let's buy tickets for home!"

But she only shook her head. "One day the atom bomb will fix Earth. Then we'll be safe here."

"Safe and insane!"

Tick-tock, seven o'clock sang the voice-clock; *time to get up.* And they did.

Something made him check everything each morning—warm hearth,[3] potted blood-geraniums— precisely as if he expected something to be amiss. The morning paper was toast-warm from the 6 A.M. Earth rocket. He broke its seal and tilted it at his breakfast place. He forced himself to be convivial.[4]

"Colonial days all over again," he declared. "Why, in ten years there'll be a million Earthmen on Mars. Big cities, everything! They said we'd fail. Said the Martians would resent our invasion. But did we find any Martians? Not a living soul! Oh, we found their empty cities, but no one in them. Right?"

3. **hearth** [härth]: fireside, home.
4. **convivial** [kən viv′ ē əl]: sociable, jovial.

A river of wind submerged the house. When the windows ceased rattling, Mr. Bittering swallowed and looked at the children.

"I don't know," said David. "Maybe there're Martians around we don't see. Sometimes nights I think I hear 'em. I hear the wind. The sand hits my window. I get scared. And I see those towns way up in the mountains where the Martians lived a long time ago. And I think I see things moving around those towns, Papa. And I wonder if those Martians *mind* us living here. I wonder if they won't do something to us for coming here."

"Nonsense!" Mr. Bittering looked out the window. "We're clean, decent people." He looked at his children. "All dead cities have some kind of ghosts in them. Memories, I mean." He stared at the hills, "You see a staircase and you wonder what Martians looked like climbing it. You see Martian paintings and you wonder what the painter was like. You make a little ghost in your mind, a memory. It's quite natural. Imagination." He stopped. "You haven't been prowling up in those ruins, have you?"

"No, Papa." David looked at his shoes.

"See that you stay away from them. Pass the jam."

"Just the same," said little David, "I bet something happens."

Something happened that afternoon.

Laura stumbled through the settlement, crying. She dashed blindly onto the porch.

"Mother, Father—the war, Earth!" she sobbed. "A radio flash just came. Atom bombs hit New York! All the space rockets blown up. No more rockets to Mars, ever!"

"Oh, Harry!" The mother held onto her husband and daughter.

"Are you sure, Laura?" asked the father quietly.

Laura wept. "We're stranded on Mars, forever and ever!"

For a long time there was only the sound of the wind in the late afternoon.

Alone, thought Bittering. Only a thousand of us here. No way back. No way. No way. Sweat poured from his face and his hands and his body; he was drenched in the hotness of his fear. He wanted to strike Laura, cry, "No, you're lying! The rockets will come back!" Instead, he stroked Laura's head against him and said, "The rockets will get through someday."

"Father, what will we do?"

"Go about our business, of course. Raise crops and children. Wait. Keep things going until the war ends and the rockets come again."

The two boys stepped out onto the porch.

"Children," he said, sitting there, looking beyond them, "I've something to tell you."

"We know," they said.

In the following days, Bittering wandered often through the garden to stand alone in his fear. As long as the rockets had spun a silver web across space, he had been able to accept Mars. For he had always told himself: Tomorrow, if I want, I can buy a ticket and go back to Earth.

But now: the web gone, the rockets lying in jigsaw heaps of molten[5] girder and unsnaked wire: Earth people left to the strangeness of Mars, the cinnamon dusts and wine airs, to be baked like gingerbread shapes in Martian summers, put into harvested storage by Martian winters. What would happen to him, the others? This was the moment Mars had waited for. Now it would eat them.

He got down on his knees in the flower bed, a spade in his nervous hands. Work, he thought, work and forget.

He glanced up from the garden to the Martian mountains. He thought of the proud old Martian names that had once been on those peaks. Earthmen, dropping from the sky, had gazed upon hills, rivers, Martian seas left nameless in spite of names. Once Martians had built cities, named cites; climbed mountains, named mountains; sailed seas, named seas. Mountains melted, seas drained, cities tumbled. In spite of this, the Earthmen had felt a silent guilt at putting new names to these ancient hills and valleys.

Nevertheless, man lives by symbol and label. The names were given.

Mr. Bittering felt very alone in his garden under the Martian sun, an anachronism[6] bent here, planting Earth flowers in a wild soil.

Think. Keep thinking. Different things. Keep your mind free of Earth, the atom war, the lost rockets.

He perspired. He glanced about. No one watching. He

5. **molten** [mōlt′n]: made liquid by heat.
6. **anachronism** [ə nak′rə niz′əm]: out of keeping with the time in which he is living.

removed his tie. Pretty bold, he thought. First your coat off, now your tie. He hung it neatly on a peach tree he had imported as a sapling[7] from Massachusetts.

He returned to his philosophy of names and mountains. The Earthmen had changed names. Now there were Hormel Valleys, Roosevelt Seas, Ford Hills, Vanderbilt Plateaus, Rockefeller Rivers, on Mars. It wasn't right. The American settlers had shown wisdom, using old Indian prairie names: Wisconsin, Minnesota, Idaho, Ohio, Utah, Milwaukee, Waukegan, Osseo. The old names, the old meanings.

Staring at the mountains wildly, he thought: Are you up there? All the dead ones, you Martians? Well, here we are, alone, cut off! Come down, move us out! We're helpless!

The wind blew a shower of peach blossoms.

He put out his sun-browned hand, gave a small cry. He touched the blossoms, picked them up. He turned them, he touched them again and again. Then he shouted for his wife.

"Cora!"

She appeared at a window. He ran to her.

"Cora, these blossoms!"

She handled them.

"Do you see? They're different. They've changed! They're not peach blossoms any more!"

"Look all right to me," she said.

"They're not. They're *wrong*! I can't tell how. An extra petal, a leaf, something; the color, the smell!"

The children ran out in time to see their father hurrying about the garden, pulling up radishes, onions, and carrots from their beds.

"Cora, come look!"

They handled the onions, the radishes, the carrots among them.

"Do they look like carrots?"

"Yes . . . no." She hesitated. "I don't know."

"They've changed."

"Perhaps."

"You know they have! Onions but not onions, carrots but not carrots. Taste: the same but different. Smell: not like it used to be." He felt his heart pounding, and he was afraid. He dug his fingers into the earth. "Cora, what's happening?

7. **sapling:** a young tree.

The Naming of Names 17

What is it? We've got to get away from this." He ran across the garden. Each tree felt his touch. "The roses. The roses. They're turning green!"

And they stood looking at the green roses.

And two days later Dan came running. "Come see the cow. I was milking her and I saw it. Come on!"

They stood in the shed and looked at their one cow.

It was growing a third horn.

And the lawn in front of their house very quietly and slowly was coloring itself like spring violets. Seed from Earth but growing up a soft purple.

"We must get away," said Bittering. "We'll eat this stuff and then we'll change—who knows to what? I can't let it happen. There's only one thing to do. Burn this food!"

"It's not poisoned."

"But it is. Subtly, very subtly. A little bit. A very little bit. We mustn't touch it."

He looked with dismay at their house.

"Even the house. The wind's done something to it. The air's burned it. The fog at night. The boards, all warped out of shape. It's not an Earthman's house any more."

"Oh, your imagination!"

He put on his coat and tie. "I'm going into town. We've got to do something now. I'll be back."

"Wait, Harry!" his wife cried.

But he was gone.

In town, on the shadowy step of the grocery store, the men sat with their hands on their knees, conversing with great leisure and ease.

Mr. Bittering wanted to fire a pistol in the air.

What are you doing, you fools! he thought. Sitting here! You've heard the news—we're stranded on this planet. Well, move! Aren't you frightened? Aren't you afraid? What are you going to do?

"Hello, Harry," said everyone.

"Look," he said to them. "You did hear the news, the other day, didn't you?"

They nodded and laughed. "Sure. Sure, Harry."

"What are you going to do about it?"

"Do, Harry, do? What *can* we do?"

"Build a rocket, that's what!"

"A rocket, Harry? To go back to all that trouble? Oh, Harry!"

"But you *must* want to go back. Have you noticed the peach blossoms, the onions, the grass?"

"Why, yes, Harry, seems we did," said one of the men.

"Doesn't it scare you?"

"Can't recall that it did much, Harry."

"Idiots!"

"Now, Harry."

Bittering wanted to cry. "You've got to work with me. If we stay here, we'll all change. The air. Don't you smell it? Something in the air. A Martian virus, maybe; some seed, or a pollen. Listen to me!"

They stared at him.

"Sam," he said to one of them.

"Yes, Harry?"

"Will you help me build a rocket?"

"Harry, I got a whole load of metal and some blueprints. You want to work in my metal shop on a rocket, you're welcome. I'll sell you that metal for five hundred dollars. You should be able to construct a right[8] pretty rocket, if you work alone, in about thirty years."

Everyone laughed.

"Don't laugh."

Sam looked at him with quiet good humor.

"Sam," Bittering said. "Your eyes—"

"What about them, Harry?"

"Didn't they used to be gray?"

"Well, now, I don't remember."

"They were, weren't they?"

"Why do you ask, Harry?"

"Because now they're kind of yellow-colored."

"Is that so, Harry?" Sam said, casually.

"And you're taller and thinner—"

"You might be right, Harry."

"Sam, you shouldn't have yellow eyes."

"Harry, what color eyes have *you* got?" Sam said.

"My eyes? They're blue, of course."

"Here you are, Harry," Sam handed him a pocket mirror. "Take a look at yourself."

Mr. Bittering hesitated and then raised the mirror to his face.

There were little, very dim flecks of new gold captured in the blue of his eyes.

"Now look what you've done," said Sam a moment later. "You've broken my mirror."

Harry Bittering moved into the metal shop and began to build the rocket. Men stood in the open door and talked and joked without

8. **right:** very.

raising their voices. Once in a while they gave him a hand on lifting something. But mostly they just idled and watched him with their yellowing eyes.

"It's suppertime, Harry," they said.

His wife appeared with his supper in a wicker basket.

I won't touch it," he said. "I'll eat only food from our deep-freeze. Food that came from Earth. Nothing from our garden."

His wife stood watching him. "You can't build a rocket."

"I worked in a shop once, when I was twenty. I know metal. Once I get it started, the others will help," he said, not looking at her, laying out the blueprints.

"Harry. Harry," she said helplessly.

"We've got to get away, Cora. We've *got* to!"

The nights were full of wind that blew down the empty moonlit sea meadows past the little white chess cities lying for their twelve-thousandth year in the shallows. In the Earthmen's settlement, the Bittering house shook with a feeling of change.

Lying abed, Mr. Bittering felt his bones shifted, shaped, melted like gold. His wife, lying beside him, was dark from many sunny afternoons. Dark she was, and golden-eyed, burnt almost black by the sun, sleeping, and the children metallic in their beds, and the wind roaring forlorn and changing through the old peach trees, the violet grass, shaking out green rose petals.

The fear would not be stopped. It had his throat and heart. It dripped in a wetness of the arm and the temple and the trembling palm.

A green star rose in the east.

A strange word emerged from Mr. Bittering's lips.

"Iorrt. Iorrt." He repeated it.

It was a Martian word. He knew no Martian.

In the middle of the night he arose and dialed a call through to Simpson, the archaeologist.[9]

"Simpson, what does the word *Iorrt* mean?"

"Why that's the old Martian word for our planet Earth. Why?"

"No special reason."

The telephone slipped from his hand.

---

9. **archaeologist** [är′ kē ol′ ə jist]: an expert in the study of people and customs of ancient times.

"Hello, hello, hello, hello," it kept saying while he sat gazing out at the green star. "Bittering? Harry, are you there?"

The days were full of metal sound. He laid the frame of the rocket with the reluctant help of three indifferent men. He grew very tired in an hour or so and had to sit down.

"The altitude," laughed a man.

"Are you *eating*, Harry?" asked another.

"I'm eating," he said, angrily.

"From your deep-freeze?"

"Yes!"

"You're getting thinner, Harry."

"I'm not!"

"And taller."

"Liar!"

His wife took him aside a few days later. "Harry, I've used up all the food in the deep-freeze. There's nothing left. I'll have to make sandwiches using food grown on Mars."

He sat down heavily.

"You must eat," she said. "You're weak."

"Yes," he said.

He took a sandwich, opened it, looked at it, and began to nibble at it.

"And take the rest of the day off," she said. "It's hot. The children want to swim in the canals and hike. Please come along."

"I can't waste time. This is a crisis!"

"Just for an hour," she urged. "A swim'll do you good."

He rose, sweating. "All right, all right. Leave me alone. I'll come."

The sun was hot, the day quiet. There was only an immense staring burn upon the land. They moved along the canal, the father, the mother, the racing children in their swim suits. They stopped and ate meat sandwiches. He saw their skin baking brown. And he saw the yellow eyes of his wife and his children, their eyes that were never yellow before. A few tremblings shook him but were carried off in waves of pleasant heat as he lay in the sun. He was too tired to be afraid.

"Cora, how long have your eyes been yellow?"

She was bewildered. "Always, I guess."

"They didn't change from brown in the last three months?"

She bit her lips. "No. Why do you ask?"

"Never mind."

They sat there.

"The children's eyes," he said. "They're yellow, too."

"Sometimes growing children's eyes change color."

"Maybe *we're* children, too. At least to Mars. That's a thought." He laughed. "Think I'll swim."

They leaped into the canal water, and he let himself sink down and down to the bottom like a golden statue and lie there in green silence. All was water—quiet and deep, all was peace. He felt the steady, slow current drift him easily.

If I lie here long enough, he thought, the water will work and eat away my flesh until the bones show like coral.[10] Just my skeleton left. And then the water can build on that skeleton—green things, deep water things, red things, yellow things. Change. Change. Slow, deep, silent change. And isn't that what it is up *there?*

He saw the sky submerged above him, the sun made Martian by atmosphere and time and space.

Up there, a big river, he thought, a Martian river, all of us lying deep in it, in our pebble houses, in our sunken boulder houses, like crayfish hidden, and the water washing away our old bodies and lengthening the bones and—

He let himself drift up through the soft light.

Dan sat on the edge of the canal, regarding his father seriously.

"Utha," he said.

"What?" asked his father.

The boy smiled. "You know. *Utha's* the Martian word for 'father.'"

"Where did you learn it?"

"I don't know. Around. *Utha!*"

"What do you want?"

The boy hesitated. "I—I want to change my name."

"Change it?"

"Yes."

His mother swam over. "What's wrong with Dan for a name?"

Dan fidgeted. "The other day you called Dan, Dan, Dan. I said to myself, 'That's not my name. I've a new name I want to use.'"

Mr. Bittering held to the side of the canal, his body cold and his heart pounding slowly. "What is this new name?"

"Linnl. Isn't that a good name? Can I use it? Can I, please?"

Mr. Bittering put his hand to his head. He thought of the silly rocket, himself working alone,

10. **coral** [kôr′ əl]: stony substance formed from the skeletons of tropical sea animals called polyps.

himself alone even among his family, so alone.

He heard his wife say, "Why not?"

He heard himself say, "Yes, you can use it."

"Yaaa!" screamed the boy. "I'm Linnl, Linnl."

Racing down the meadowlands, he danced and shouted.

Mr. Bittering looked at his wife. "Why did we do that?"

"I don't know," she said. "It just seemed like a good idea."

They walked into the hills. They strolled on old mosaic[11] paths, beside still pumping fountains. The paths were covered with a thin film of cool water all summer long. They kept their bare feet cool all the day, splashing as in a creek, wading.

They came to a small deserted Martian villa[12] with a good view of the valley. It was on top of a hill. Blue marble halls, large murals, a swimming pool. It was refreshing in this hot summertime. The Martians hadn't believed in large cities.

"How nice," said Mrs. Bittering, "if we could move up here to this villa for the summer."

"Come on," he said. "We're going back to town. There's work to be done on the rocket."

But as he worked that night, the thought of the cool blue marble villa entered his mind. As the hours passed, the rocket seemed less important.

In the flow of days and weeks, the rocket receded and dwindled. The old fever was gone. It frightened him to think he had let it slip this way. But somehow the heat, the air, the working conditions—

He heard the men murmuring on the porch of his metal shop.

"Everyone's going. You heard?"

"All going. That's right."

Bittering came out. "Going where?" He saw a couple of trucks, loaded with children and furniture, drive down the dusty street.

"Up to the villas," said the man.

"Yeah, Harry. I'm going. So is Sam. Aren't you, Sam?"

"That's right, Harry. What about you?"

"I've got work to do here."

"Work! You can finish that rocket in the autumn, when it's cooler."

11. **mosaic** [mō zāʹ ik]: decoration made of small colored pieces of stone, glass, or wood inlaid to form a picture or design.

12. **villa:** large elegant house.

He took a breath. "I got the frame all set up."

"In the autumn is better." Their voices were lazy in the heat.

"Got to work," he said.

"Autumn," they reasoned. And they sounded so sensible, so right.

"Autumn would be best," he thought. "Plenty of time, then."

No! cried part of himself, deep down, put away, locked tight, suffocating. No! No!

"In the autumn," he said.

"Come on, Harry," they all said.

"Yes, in the autumn. I'll begin work again then."

"I got a villa near the Tirra Canal," said someone.

"You mean the Roosevelt Canal, don't you?"

"Tirra. The old Martian name."

"But on the map—"

"Forget the map. It's Tirra now. Now I found a place in the Pillan Mountains—"

"You mean the Rockefeller Range," said Bittering.

"I mean the Pillan Mountains," said Sam.

"Yes," said Bittering, buried in the hot, swarming air. "The Pillan Mountains."

Everyone worked at loading the truck in the hot, still afternoon of the next day.

Laura, Dan, David carried packages. Or, as they preferred to be known, Ttil, Linnl, and Werr carried packages.

The furniture was abandoned in the little white cottage.

"It looked just fine in Boston," said the mother. "And here in the cottage. But up at the villa? No. We'll get it when we come back in the autumn."

Bittering himself was quiet.

"I've got some ideas on furniture for the villa," he said after a time. "Big, lazy furniture."

"What about your encyclopedia? You're taking it along, surely?"

Mr. Bittering glanced away. "I'll come and get it next week."

They turned to their daughter. "What about your New York dresses?"

The bewildered girl stared. "Why, I don't want them anymore."

They shut off the gas, the water; they locked the doors and walked away. Father peered into the truck.

"Gosh, we're not taking much," he said. "Considering all we brought to Mars, this is only a handful!"

He started the truck.

Looking at the small white cottage for a long moment, he was filled with a desire to rush to it, touch it, say goodbye to it, for he felt as if he were going away on a long journey, leaving something to which he could never quite return, never understand again.

Just then Sam and his family drove by in another truck.

"Hi Bittering! Here we go!"

The truck swung down the ancient highway out of town. There were sixty others traveling the same direction. The town filled with a silent, heavy dust from their passage. The canal waters lay blue in the sun, and a quiet wind moved in the strange trees.

"Good-by town!" said Mr. Bittering.

"Good-by, good-by!" sang the family, waving to it.

They did not look back again.

Summer burned the canals dry. Summer moved like flame upon the meadows. In the empty Earth settlement, the painted houses flaked and peeled. Rubber tires upon which children had swung in back yards hung suspended like stopped clock pendulums in the blazing air.

At the metal shop, the rocket frame began to rust.

In the quiet autumn Mr. Bittering stood, very dark now, very golden-eyed, upon the slope above his villa, looking at the valley.

"It's time to go back," said Cora.

"Yes, but we're not going," he said quietly. "There's nothing there any more."

"Your books," she said. "Your fine clothes. Your *lles* and your fine *ior uele rre*."

"The town's empty. No one's going back," he said. "There's no reason to, none at all."

The daughter wove tapestries and the sons played songs on ancient flutes and pipes, their laughter echoing in the marble villa.

Mr. Bittering gazed at the Earth settlement far away in the low valley. "Such odd, such ridiculous houses the Earth people built."

"They didn't know any better," his wife mused. "Such ugly people. I'm glad they've gone."

They both looked at each other, startled by all they had just finished saying. They laughed.

"Where did they go?" he

wondered. He glanced at his wife. She was golden and slender as his daughter. She looked at him, and he seemed almost as young as their eldest son.

"I don't know," she said.

"We'll go back to town maybe next year, or the year after, or the year after that," he said, calmly. "Now—I'm warm. How about taking a swim?"

They turned their backs to the valley. Arm in arm they walked silently down a path of clear-running spring water . . .

Five years later a rocket fell out of the sky. It lay steaming in the valley. Men leaped out of it shouting.

"We won the war on Earth! We're here to rescue you! Hey!"

But the American-built town of cottages, peach trees, and theaters was silent. They found a flimsy rocket frame rusting in an empty shop.

The rocket men searched the hills. The captain established headquarters in an abandoned building. His lieutenant came back to report.

"The town's empty, but we found native life in the hills, sir. Dark people. Yellow eyes. Martians. Very friendly. We talked a bit, not much. They learned English fast. I'm sure our relations will be most friendly with them, sir."

"Dark, eh?" mused the captain. "How many?"

"Six, eight hundred, I'd say, living in those marble ruins in the hills, sir. Tall, healthy. Beautiful women."

"Did they tell you what became of the men and women who built this Earth settlement, Lieutenant?"

"They hadn't the foggiest notion of what happened to this town or its people."

"Strange. You think those Martians killed them?"

"They look surprisingly peaceful. Chances are a plague[13] did this town in, sir."

"Perhaps. I suppose this is one of those mysteries we'll never solve. One of those mysteries you read about."

The captain looked at the room, the dusty windows, the blue mountains rising beyond, the canals moving in the light, and he

13. **plague** [plāg]: highly contagious, often fatal, disease that spreads quickly and affects large numbers of people.

heard the soft wind in the air. He shivered. Then, recovering, he tapped a large fresh map he had thumb-tacked to the top of an empty table.

"Lots to be done, Lieutenant." His voice droned on and on quietly as the sun sank behind the blue hills. "New settlements. Mining sites, minerals to be looked for. Bacteriological specimens taken. The work, all the work. And the old records were lost. We'll have a job of remapping to do, renaming the mountains and rivers and such. Calls for a little imagination.

"What do you think of naming those mountains the Lincoln Mountains, this canal the Washington Canal, those hills— we can name those hills for you, Lieutenant. Diplomacy. And you, for a favor, might name a town for me. Polishing the apple. And why not make this the Einstein Valley, and further over. . . . Are you *listening*, Lieutenant?"

The lieutenant snapped his gaze from the blue color and the quiet mist of the hills far beyond the town.

"What? Oh, *yes*, sir!"

R A Y   B R A D B U R Y

Ray Bradbury was born in 1920 in Waukegan, Illinois. When he was a child, he loved reading comic strips. The imaginative cartoon adventures helped to develop his taste for what he calls "the fabulous world of the future and the world of fantasy." As he grew older, he spent his spare time learning magic tricks, and he soon began writing space adventures.

By the time Bradbury graduated from high school, he was churning out 2,000 words per day, and the country was struggling through the Great Depression. He sold newspapers on a street corner and continued to write. Oddly enough, the writer of so many words prefers writing short stories to novels—and his novels are more like short stories. One of his most famous works, *The Martian Chronicles,* is a book of connected stories. Bradbury has also turned some of his short stories into scripts for plays, movies, and television programs.

Song of the Earth Spirit

TRADITIONAL NAVAJO

It is lovely indeed; it is lovely indeed.

I, I am the spirit within the earth.

The feet of the earth are my feet;

The legs of the earth are my legs;

The strength of the earth is my strength;   5

The thoughts of the earth are my thoughts;

The voice of the earth is my voice;

The feather of the earth is my feather.

All that belongs to the earth belongs to me;

All that surrounds the earth surrounds me.   10

I, I am the sacred words of the earth.

It is lovely indeed; it is lovely indeed.

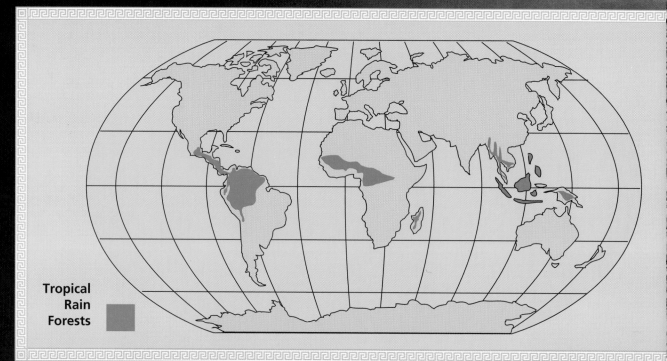

Tropical Rain Forests

Makuna Children,
Amazon, Colombia

Paradise Lost

ELIZABETH VITTON

Zap! From below the surface, an archerfish[1] blasts an unwary spider on a leaf with a bullet of water. The spider drops into the pool and is gobbled up. Downstream, a piglike tapir[2] searches for food with its multi-purpose trunk. Above the jungle floor, a troop of monkeys chatters while birds streak by, their wings weaving a tapestry of brilliant colors.

Welcome to the rain forest, an exotic world where the air is thick mist, where fish walk on land, where passion flowers bloom and tree frogs sing. A place where the constant hum of thousands of animals fills the air.

1. **archerfish:** small fresh-water fish of Southeast Asia that preys upon spiders and insects on shore by spitting drops of water at them to knock them into the water.
2. **tapir** [tā′ pər]: large mammal of the tropics having hooves and a flexible snout.

Left, Red-Eyed Tree Frog

Background, Rain Forest Burning, Amazon, Brazil

But now the roar of the chain saw is drowning out the jungle chorus. "Each minute, 100 acres of the world's jungles are being cut and burned," says Dr. Stuart Strahl of Wildlife Conservation International. "At this rate, nearly all the Earth's tropical rain forests will either be destroyed or seriously damaged by the year 2035."

Most rain forests are found in the tropics bordering either side of the equator, like a wide belt circling the Earth. Rain forests get an average of 100 to 400 inches of rain per year. The heavy rainfall may make the forest green, but it also washes away a lot of nutrients from the soil. Because of this, the shallow-rooted trees get most of their nourishment from leaves and dead materials that fall from above.

As they compete for sunlight, trees in the tropical forest grow to amazing heights—50 to 150 feet—before sprouting branches and leaves. Below the tentlike canopy of trees grow palms, looping vines, orchids, ferns and other plants. Less than two percent of the sunlight that nourishes the canopy ever reaches the floor. But even there many plant and animal species thrive in a twilight world.

New species are being discovered all the time in the rain forest. Right now nearly two *million* species have been named. "And for every jungle species known, there remain 40 yet undiscovered," says Dr. Fred Kuntz. He is a mammal expert at the Bronx Zoo in New York. "We know more about distant planets than the nearest rain forest!"

Even though rain forests cover only six percent of the Earth, they are home to more

Parson's Chameleon, Madagascar

than half of all living things on our planet. Scores of these plants and animals are now dying out. "Nearly 10,000 species are already being lost every year, never to be replaced," Dr. Kuntz told CONTACT. "Once a species is lost, it's gone forever."

It's Not Easy Being Green

Why are we losing so much of our rain forests? Most of the tropical rain forests lie in poor nations whose populations are growing very quickly. Since they have no big industries, Dr. Strahl says, they make money by using the resources in the forest.

"It takes minutes for a chain saw to topple a seven-foot-wide tree, but it will take five centuries for another tree to grow to the same size," says Matthew Hatchwell. He works to help save the Earth's rain forests. The crashing timber destroys small trees lying in its path. Tractors flatten more forest when they drag the trunks to loading areas.

As roads are cut to get the logs to market, it opens up the area to a flood of people who burn parts of the jungle to make room for farms and ranches. The problem is that most of the nutrients are in the living trees—not in the topsoil. So if the forest is cut down and burned, there is a very thin layer of rich ash which can grow crops for a few years. But once the nutrients have been used up by the crops or been

Volcan Barva Bromeliads, Costa Rica

Bee Butterfly, Trinidad

35

Jaguar, Belize

Passion Flower, South America

washed away by the warm rains, the land becomes almost worthless. "When the soil gives out," Hatchwell told CONTACT, "it forces farmers to clear more and more land."

Destroying rain forests as far away as Brazil[3] and Indonesia[4] has serious consequences for all of us. For example, the world needs trees to recycle carbon dioxide (CO_2), an odorless gas. Rain forests are the "lungs" of the planet. They suck the CO_2 out of the atmosphere through their leaves. The trees then "breathe" oxygen back into the atmosphere and pump it with moisture that falls as rain.

3. **Brazil** [brə zil′]: country in central and northeast South America on the Atlantic Ocean.
4. **Indonesia** [in′ də nē′ zhə]: country in the East Indies, south of Vietnam, northwest of Australia.

But trees are about 50 percent carbon.[5] If they are burned, the CO_2 trapped inside them is released. "It's a double whammy," explains Dr. Russell Mittermeier, a conservationist. "The burning itself releases huge amounts of CO_2. And it reduces the trees available to absorb the gas."

Carbon dioxide is a "greenhouse" gas. Like a greenhouse, carbon dioxide lets the sun's incoming rays through, but blocks reflected rays from leaving the atmosphere. It traps the sun's heat. But many scientists believe that too much carbon dioxide could cause the Earth to heat up. The "greenhouse effect" would do more than just cause the temperature to rise, says Dr. Strahl. "It would also affect winds, rainfall, sea levels and storms. We need rain forests to help control our climate."

Food for Thought

Rain forests do more than help provide oxygen to the planet. They also help save lives in other ways, too. In fact, one-quarter of prescription drugs used in the U.S. come from tropical forest plants. Most plants, though, haven't been studied for ways to treat diseases. Says Dr. Mittermeier: "For all we know, solutions to health problems like cancer may exist in tropical forests."

Rain forests put medicine in your cabinet as well as food on your table. Each day people eat or

Tarsier with Cicada, Sabah, Borneo

5. **carbon:** a nonmetallic element found in plants and animals.

Rafflesia Keithii,
Mt. Kinabalu, Borneo

Morpho Butterfly, Peru

drink something that comes from the jungle. Fruits, nuts, spices, coffee, sugar cane, cocoa and even chickens originated in rain forests. "Many are now grown elsewhere," Mittermeier says, "but if a pest[6] attacks, a crop could be wiped out. So we have to be able to go back to the rain forest to crossbreed[7] commercial crops with their relatives from the wild."

Rain forests also provide us with common workday tools, such as burlap bags and rope nets. Fibers used for stuffing pillows and life jackets come from the jungle. So do the oils of many perfumes. Some jungle products have surprising uses, says Strahl. "Take M&Ms. The candy doesn't melt in your hand because they're coated with a harmless wax, which comes from tropical forests."

What's being done to save the globe's greatest natural treasury? Some poorer countries, like Costa Rica and Bolivia, have promised to protect their forests in exchange for lessening the money they owe to other nations. Others are setting aside nature reserves and planting new trees.

In Brazil, a rubber tappers' union is fighting for large areas to be set aside just for rubber production and the collection of fruits and nuts. In Malaysia, the Penan[8] people set up human blockades to try

6. **pest:** destructive or harmful insect.
7. **crossbreed:** make new crops by interbreeding different varieties of plants.
8. **Penan** [pē′nän]: people of Penang, an island that is part of Malaysia.

to stop logging on their lands. In Papua New Guinea, many ranchers now earn a living by raising herds of butterflies, crocodiles and wallabies[9] instead of cattle, which destroy the land.

Time will tell whether efforts like these succeed in saving the world's emerald[10] forests. "I see it as a race against time," says Dr. Strahl. "We have the power to save or destroy the rain forests. The fate of millions of species is on our shoulders."

9. **wallabies** [wol′ ə bēz]: small or medium-sized kangaroos.
10. **emerald:** green.

Golden Beetle, Cloud Forest, Costa Rica

ELIZABETH VITTON

Elizabeth Vitton was born in Warner Robins, Georgia. She attended Vassar College and then taught high school English. She eventually moved to New York City, where she worked in textbook publishing and finally for magazines. As Vitton says, teaching and publishing made up "the route I took to my goal of working for *3-2-1 Contact*," a magazine published by Children's Television Workshop.

Vitton wrote "Paradise Lost" because of her concern for the environment. She says, "We know that kids are environmentally concerned. They are very aware—and not only of the plight of endangered species. Kids are the advocates" for saving the rainforest and for solving other problems people have caused on Earth. In their role as advocates, Vitton suggests that young people "learn to do original research: first find the most up-to-date books, then talk to experts in the field and conservation groups."

HARRISON BERGERON

KURT VONNEGUT, JR.

The year was 2081, and everybody was finally equal. They weren't only equal before God and the law. They were equal every which way. Nobody was smarter than anybody else. Nobody was better looking than anybody else. Nobody was stronger or quicker than anybody else. All this equality was due to the 211th, 212th, and the 213th Amendments to the Constitution, and to the unceasing vigilance of agents of the United States Handicapper[1] General.

Some things about living still weren't quite right, though. April, for instance, still drove people crazy by not being springtime. And it was in that clammy month that the H-G men took George and Hazel Bergeron's fourteen-year-old son, Harrison, away.

---

1. **Handicapper:** reference to the custom in games of giving less skilled people advantages and more skilled people disadvantages so that all have an equal chance for victory.

It was tragic, all right, but George and Hazel couldn't think about it very hard. Hazel had a perfectly average intelligence, which meant she couldn't think about anything except in short bursts. And George, while his intelligence was way above normal, had a little mental handicap radio in his ear. He was required by law to wear it at all times. It was tuned to a government transmitter. Every twenty seconds or so, the transmitter would send out some sharp noise to keep people like George from taking unfair advantage of their brains.

George and Hazel were watching television. There were tears on Hazel's cheeks, but she'd forgotten for the moment what they were about.

On the television screen were ballerinas.

A buzzer sounded in George's head. His thoughts fled in panic, like bandits from a burglar alarm.

"That was a real pretty dance, that dance they just did," said Hazel.

"Huh?" said George.

"That dance—it was nice," said Hazel.

"Yup," said George. He tried to think a little about the ballerinas. They weren't really very good—no better than anybody else would have been, anyway. They were burdened with sash-weights[2] and bags of birdshot,[3] and their faces were masked, so that no one, seeing a free and graceful gesture or a pretty face, would feel like something the cat drug in.[4] George was toying with the vague notion that maybe dancers shouldn't be handicapped. But he didn't get very far before another noise in his ear radio scattered his thoughts.

George winced.[5] So did two out of the eight ballerinas.

Hazel saw him wince. Having no mental handicap herself, she had to ask George what the latest sound had been.

"Sounded like somebody hitting a milk bottle with a ball peen hammer,"[6] said George.

2. **sash-weights:** metal weights in windows that allow them to be raised and lowered.
3. **birdshot:** small lead pellets usually used in shooting birds.
4. **something the cat drug in:** idiom that means someone looks terrible.
5. **winced:** drew back suddenly.
6. **ball peen hammer:** hammer that has a rounded or wedged head.

"I'd think it would be real interesting, hearing all the different sounds," said Hazel, a little envious. "All the things they think up."

"Um," said George.

"Only, if I was Handicapper General, you know what I would do?" asked Hazel. Hazel, as a matter of fact, bore a strong resemblance to the Handicapper General, a woman named Diana Moon Glampers. "If I was Diana Moon Glampers," said Hazel, "I'd have chimes[7] on Sunday—just chimes. Kind of in honor of religion."

"I could think, if it was just chimes," said George.

"Well—maybe make 'em real loud," said Hazel. "I think I'd make a good Handicapper General."

"Good as anybody else," said George.

"Who knows better'n I do what normal is?" said Hazel.

"Right," said George. He began to think glimmeringly[8] about his abnormal son who was now in jail, about Harrison, but a twenty-one-gun salute[9] in his head stopped that.

"Boy!" said Hazel, "that was a doozy,[10] wasn't it?"

It was such a doozy that George was white and trembling, and tears stood on the rims of his red eyes. Two of the eight ballerinas had collapsed to the studio floor, and were holding their temples.[11]

"All of a sudden you look so tired," said Hazel. "Why don't you stretch out on the sofa, so's you can rest your handicap bag on the pillows, honeybunch." She was referring to the forty-seven pounds of birdshot in a canvas bag, which was padlocked around George's neck. "Go on and rest the bag for awhile," she said. "I don't care if you're not equal to me for awhile."

George weighed the bag with his hands. "I don't mind it," he said. "I don't notice it any more. It's just part of me."

---

7. **chimes:** set of bells, usually in church towers, tuned to a musical scale.
8. **glimmeringly:** with a dim perception or faint idea
9. **twenty-one-gun salute:** usually, firing of cannons as a sign of respect for a famous person.
10. **doozy** [dü′ zē]: something outstanding or unusual.
11. **temples:** the flattened part on each side of the forehead.

"You've been so tired lately—kind of wore out," said Hazel. "If there was just some way we could make a little hole in the bottom of the bag, and just take out a few of them lead balls. Just a few."

"Two years in prison and two thousand dollars fine for every ball I took out," said George. "I don't call that a bargain."

"If you could just take a few out when you come home from work," said Hazel. "I mean—you don't compete with anybody around here. You just set around."

"If I tried to get away with it," said George, "then other people'd get away with it—and pretty soon we'd be right back to the dark ages again, with everybody competing against everybody else. You wouldn't like that, would you?"

"I'd hate it," said Hazel.

"There you are," said George. "The minute people start cheating on laws, what do you think happens to society?"

If Hazel hadn't been able to come up with an answer to this question, George couldn't have supplied one. A siren was going off in his head.

"Reckon it'd fall apart," said Hazel.

"What would?" said George blankly.

"Society," said Hazel uncertainly. "Wasn't that what you just said?"

"Who knows?" said George.

The television program was suddenly interrupted for a news bulletin. It wasn't clear at first as to what the bulletin was about, since the announcer, like all announcers, had a serious speech impediment.[12] For about half a minute, and in a state of high excitement, the announcer tried to say, "Ladies and gentlemen—"

He finally gave up, handed the bulletin to a ballerina to read.

"That's all right—" Hazel said of the announcer, "he tried. That's the big thing. He tried to do the best he could with what God gave him. He should get a nice raise for trying so hard."

12. **speech impediment** [im ped′ ə mənt]: a problem that interferes with clear speech.

Untitled Francesco Clemente, 1986, Monotype
(35), 36³/₄"x20"

"Ladies and gentlemen—" said the ballerina, reading the bulletin. She must have been extraordinarily beautiful, because the mask she wore was hideous. And it was easy to see that she was the strongest and most graceful of all the dancers, for her handicap bags were as big as those worn by two-hundred-pound men.

And she had to apologize at once for her voice, which was a very unfair voice for a woman to use. Her voice was a warm, luminous,[13] timeless melody. "Excuse me—" she said, and she began again, making her voice absolutely uncompetitive.

"Harrison Bergeron, age fourteen," she said in a grackle squawk,[14] "has just escaped from jail, where he was held on suspicion of plotting to overthrow the government. He is a genius and an athlete, is underhandicapped, and should be regarded as extremely dangerous."

A police photograph of Harrison Bergeron was flashed on the screen—upside down, then sideways, then upside down again, then right side up. The picture showed the full length of Harrison against a background calibrated[15] in feet and inches. He was exactly seven feet tall.

The rest of Harrison's appearance was Halloween and hardware. Nobody had ever borne heavier handicaps. He had outgrown hindrances[16] faster than the H-G men could think them up. Instead of a little ear radio for a mental handicap, he wore a tremendous pair of earphones, and spectacles with thick wavy lenses. The spectacles were intended to make him not only half blind, but to give him whanging headaches besides.

Scrap metal was hung all over him. Ordinarily, there was a certain symmetry,[17] a military neatness to the handicaps issued to strong people, but Harrison looked like a walking junkyard. In the race of life, Harrison carried three hundred pounds.

13. **luminous** [lü′ mə nəs]: clear.
14. **grackle squawk:** the harsh sound made by a large blackbird with shiny feathers.
15. **calibrated** [kal′ ə brāt əd]: checked or adjusted by comparing to a standard instrument.
16. **hindrances** [hin′ drəns əz]: things that hold someone back from accomplishing a goal.
17. **symmetry** [sim′ ə trē]: a regular, balanced arrangement that is the same on each side.

And to offset[18] his good looks, the H-G men required that he wear at all times a red rubber ball for a nose, keep his eyebrows shaved off, and cover his even white teeth with black caps at snaggle-tooth random.

"If you see this boy," said the ballerina, "do not—I repeat, do not—try to reason with him."

There was the shriek of a door being torn from its hinges.

Screams and barking cries of consternation came from the television set. The photograph of Harrison Bergeron on the screen jumped again and again, as though dancing to the tune of an earthquake.

George Bergeron correctly identified the earthquake, and well he might have—for many was the time his own home had danced to the same crashing tune. "My God—" said George, "that must be Harrison!"

The realization was blasted from his mind instantly by the sound of an automobile collision in his head.

When George could open his eyes again, the photograph of Harrison was gone. A living, breathing Harrison filled the screen.

Clanking, clownish, and huge, Harrison stood in the center of the studio. The knob of the uprooted studio door was still in his hand. Ballerinas, technicians, musicians, and announcers cowered on their knees before him, expecting to die.

"I am the Emperor!" cried Harrison. "Do you hear? I am the Emperor! Everybody must do what I say at once!" He stamped his foot and the studio shook.

"Even as I stand here—" he bellowed, "crippled, hobbled, sickened—I am a greater ruler than any man who ever lived! Now watch me become what I can become!"

Harrison tore the straps of his handicap harness like wet tissue paper, tore straps guaranteed to support five thousand pounds.

Harrison's scrap-iron handicaps crashed to the floor.

Harrison thrust his thumbs under the bar of the padlock that secured his head harness. The bar snapped like celery. Harrison smashed his headphones and spectacles against the wall.

18. **offset:** make up for.

He flung away his rubber-ball nose, revealed a man that would have awed Thor,[19] the god of thunder.

"I shall now select my Empress!" he said, looking down on the cowering people. "Let the first woman who dares rise to her feet claim her mate and her throne!"

A moment passed, and then a ballerina arose, swaying like a willow.

Harrison plucked the mental handicap from her ear, snapped off her physical handicaps with marvelous delicacy. Last of all, he removed her mask.

She was blindingly beautiful.

"Now—" said Harrison, taking her hand, "shall we show the people the meaning of the word dance? Music!" he commanded.

The musicians scrambled back into their chairs, and Harrison stripped them of their handicaps, too. "Play your best," he told them, "and I'll make you barons and dukes and earls."

The music began. It was normal at first—cheap, silly, false. But Harrison snatched two musicians from their chairs, waved them like batons[20] as he sang the music as he wanted it played. He slammed them back into their chairs.

The music began again and was much improved.

Harrison and his Empress merely listened to the music for a while—listened gravely, as though synchronizing[21] their heart-beats with it.

They shifted their weights to their toes.

Harrison placed his big hands on the girl's tiny waist, letting her sense the weightlessness that would soon be hers.

And then, in an explosion of joy and grace, into the air they sprang!

Not only were the laws of the land abandoned, but the law of gravity and the laws of motion as well.

---

19. **Thor** [thôr].
20. **batons:** light sticks used by the leader of an orchestra, chorus, or band to indicate the beat and to direct.
21. **synchronizing** [sing′ krə nīz ing]: causing to occur at the same time; agreeing in musical time.

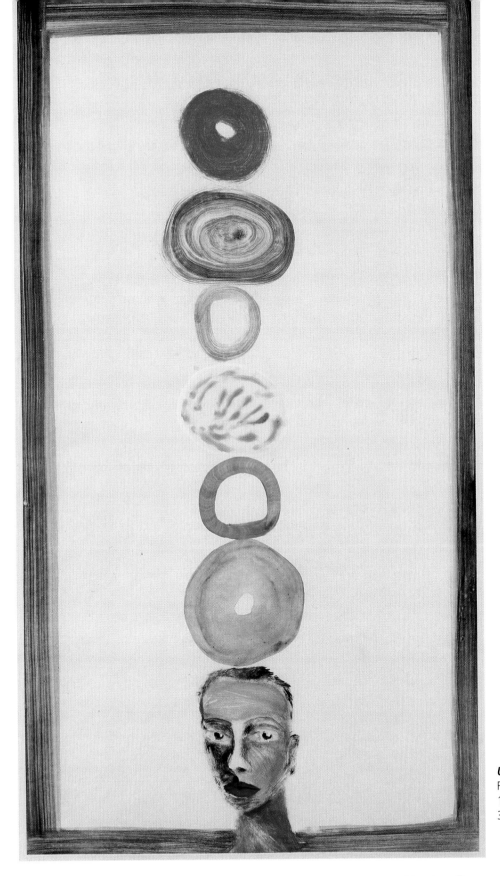

Untitled
Francesco Clemente,
1986, Monotype (4),
36 3/4"x20"

They reeled, whirled, swiveled, bounced, capered, gamboled,[22] and spun.

They leaped like deer on the moon.

The studio ceiling was thirty feet high, but each leap brought the dancers nearer to it.

It became their obvious intention to kiss the ceiling.

They kissed it.

And then, neutralizing[23] gravity with love and pure will, they remained suspended in air inches below the ceiling, and they kissed each other for a long, long time.

It was then that Diana Moon Glampers, the Handicapper General, came into the studio with a double-barreled ten-gauge shotgun. She fired twice, and the Emperor and the Empress were dead before they hit the floor.

Diana Moon Glampers loaded the gun again. She aimed it at the musicians and told them they had ten seconds to get their handicaps back on.

It was then that the Bergerons' television tube burned out.

Hazel turned to comment about the blackout to George. But George had gone into the kitchen for a can of beer.

George came back in with the beer, paused while a handicap signal shook him up. And then he sat down again. "You have been crying?" he said to Hazel.

"Yup," she said.

"What about?" he said.

"I forget," she said. "Something real sad on television."

"What was it?" he said.

"It's all kind of mixed up in my mind," said Hazel.

"Forget sad things," said George.

"I always do," said Hazel.

22. **gamboled** [gam′ bəld]: ran and jumped about.
23. **neutralizing** [nü′ trə līz ing]: cancelling.

"That's my girl," said George. He winced. There was the sound of a riveting gun[24] in his head.

"Gee—I could tell that one was a doozy," said Hazel.

"You can say that again," said George.

"Gee—" said Hazel, "I could tell that one was a doozy."

---

24. **riveting gun:** gun that drives rivets—metal bolts—into heavy material.

KURT VONNEGUT, JR.

Kurt Vonnegut, Jr. was born in 1922 in Indianapolis, Indiana, and remembers his childhood as a happy one, in spite of living through the Great Depression. Because Vonnegut's father was unemployed during the Depression years, Vonnegut went to public schools rather than to the private schools his older brother and sister had attended. The experience, however, opened a door for Vonnegut: his high school was the first in the United States to have a daily newspaper. There Vonnegut discovered the art of reporting. Following high school, Vonnegut went to Cornell University, majoring in biochemistry and writing for the campus newspaper.

World War II interrupted Vonnegut's college years. He enlisted and was sent to Europe. In 1944, he was captured by the Germans and became a prisoner of war in Dresden. When the Allies bombed Dresden in a firestorm that destroyed the city, the prisoners were fortunately among the survivors.

After the war ended, Vonnegut worked as a police reporter and did public relations work. By 1951, he was selling enough short stories to write novels full time.

ORBITER 5 SHOWS HOW EARTH LOOKS FROM THE MOON

There's a woman in the earth, sitting on her heels. You see her from the back, in three-quarter profile. She has a flowing pigtail. She's holding something in her right hand—some holy jug. Her left arm is thinner, in a gesture like a dancer. She's the Indian Ocean. Asia is light swirling up out of her vessel. Her pigtail points to Europe and her dancer's arm is the Suez Canal.[1] She is a woman in a square kimono,[2] bare feet tucked beneath the tip of Africa. Her tail of long hair is the Arabian Peninsula.[3]

A woman in the earth.

A man in the moon.

1. **Suez Canal** [sü ez′]: canal connecting the Mediterranean and Red seas.
2. **kimono** [kə mō′ nə]: loose robe held in place by a wide sash.
3. **Arabian Peninsula**: large strip of land in Southwest Asia that comprises many countries, including Saudi Arabia and Kuwait.

MAY SWENSON

May Swenson, whose concrete poem is on page 52, was born in 1919 in Logan, Utah, and grew up near the State University where her father taught. As an adult, Swenson first worked as a newspaper reporter in Salt Lake City, then she became an editor at a publishing company in New York City. After six years, she left to become a full-time poet and writer. Her first book of poems, *Another Animal*, gained critical recognition.

Swenson says that she writes many of her poems "directly on the scene . . . in much the same way as a painter sketches from life." Important collections of Swenson's poems include *To Mix with Time* and *Half Sun Half Asleep*.

"IF I FORGET THEE, OH EARTH..."

ARTHUR C. CLARKE

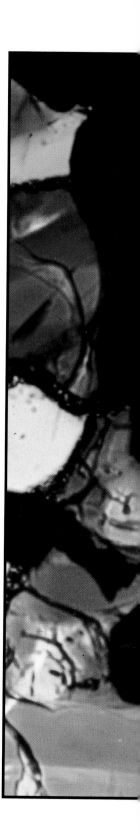

When Marvin was ten years old, his father took him through the long, echoing corridors that led up through Administration and Power, until at last they came to the uppermost levels of all and were among the swiftly growing vegetation of the Farmlands. Marvin liked it here: it was fun watching the great, slender plants creeping with almost visible eagerness towards the sunlight as it filtered down through the plastic domes to meet them. The smell of life was everywhere, awakening inexpressible longings in his heart: no longer was he breathing the dry, cool air of the residential levels, purged of all smells but the faint tang of ozone.[1] He wished he could stay here for a little while, but Father would not let him. They went onwards until they had reached the entrance to the Observatory,[2] which he had never visited: but they did not stop, and Marvin knew with a sense of rising excitement that there could be only one goal left. For the first time in his life, he was going Outside.

1. **ozone** [ō′ zōn]: form of oxygen with a sharp odor, usually present in the air, especially after a thunderstorm.
2. **Observatory** [əb zėr′ və tôr′ ē]: place for observing the stars and other heavenly bodies.

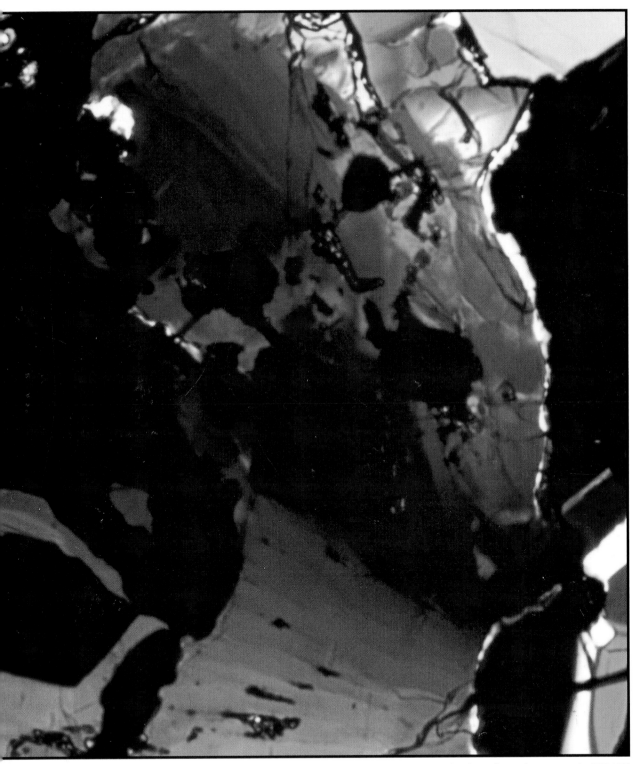

Photomicrograph of Apollo 17 lunar sample #70017

There were a dozen of the surface vehicles, with their wide balloon tires and pressurized cabins, in the great servicing chamber. His father must have been expected, for they were led at once to the little scout car waiting by the huge circular door of the airlock.[3] Tense with expectancy, Marvin settled himself down in the cramped cabin while his father started the motor and checked the controls. The inner door of the lock slid open and then closed behind them: he heard the roar of the great air-pumps fade slowly away as the pressure dropped to zero. Then the "Vacuum" sign flashed on, the outer door parted, and before Marvin lay the land which he had never yet entered.

He had seen it in photographs, of course: he had watched it imaged on television screens a hundred times. But now it was lying all around him, burning beneath the fierce sun that crawled so slowly across the jet-black sky. He stared into the west, away from the blinding splendor of the sun—and there were the stars, as he had been told but had never quite believed. He gazed at them for a long time, marveling that anything could be so bright and yet so tiny. They were intense unscintillating[4] points, and suddenly he remembered a rhyme he had once read in one of his father's books

Twinkle, twinkle, little star,
How I wonder what you are.

Well, *he* knew what the stars were. Whoever asked that question must have been very stupid. And what did they mean by "twinkle"? You could see at a glance that all the stars shone with the same steady, unwavering light. He abandoned the puzzle and turned his attention to the landscape around him.

They were racing across a level plain at almost a hundred miles an hour, the great balloon tyres sending up little spurts of dust behind them. There was no sign of the Colony: in the few minutes while he had been gazing at the stars, its domes and radio towers had

3. **airlock:** an airtight compartment between places where there is a difference in air pressure.
4. **unscintillating** [un sin′ tl āt ing]: not sparkling.

fallen below the horizon. Yet there were other indications of man's presence, for about a mile ahead Marvin could see the curiously shaped structures clustering round the head of a mine. Now and then a puff of vapor would emerge from a squat smoke-stack and would instantly disperse.

They were past the mine in a moment: Father was driving with a reckless and exhilarating[5] skill as if—it was a strange thought to come into a child's mind—he was trying to escape from something. In a few minutes they had reached the edge of the plateau on which the Colony had been built. The ground fell sharply away beneath them in a dizzying slope whose lower stretches were lost in shadow. Ahead, as far as the eye could reach, was a jumbled wasteland of craters, mountain ranges, and ravines. The crests of the mountains, catching the low sun, burned like islands of fire in a sea of darkness: and above them the stars still shone as steadfastly as ever.

There could be no way forward—yet there was. Marvin clenched his fists as the car edged over the slope and started the long descent. Then he saw the barely visible track leading down the mountainside, and relaxed a little. Other men, it seemed, had gone this way before.

Night fell with a shocking abruptness as they crossed the shadow line and the sun dropped below the crest of the plateau. The twin searchlights sprang into life, casting blue-white bands on the rocks ahead, so that there was scarcely need to check their speed. For hours they drove through valleys and past the feet of mountains whose peaks seemed to comb the stars, and sometimes they emerged for a moment into the sunlight as they climbed over higher ground.

And now on the right was a wrinkled, dusty plain, and on the left, its ramparts and terraces rising mile after mile into the sky, was a wall of mountains that marched into the distance until its peaks sank from sight below the rim of the world. There was no sign that men had ever explored this land, but once they passed the skeleton of a crashed rocket, and beside it a stone cairn[6] surmounted by a metal cross.

5. **exhilarating** [eg zil′ ə rat´ ing]: extremely energizing.
6. **cairn** [kern]: a pile of stones heaped up for a memorial or landmark.

Photomicrograph of Apollo 17 lunar sample #70017

It seemed to Marvin that the mountains stretched on forever: but at last, many hours later, the range ended in a towering, precipitous headland that rose steeply from a cluster of little hills. They drove down into a shallow valley that curved in a great arc towards the far side of the mountains: and as they did so, Marvin slowly realized that something very strange was happening in the land ahead.

The sun was now low behind the hills on the right: the valley before them should be in total darkness. Yet it was awash with a cold white radiance that came spilling over the crags beneath which they were driving. Then, suddenly, they were out in the open plain, and the source of the light lay before them in all its glory.

It was very quiet in the little cabin now that the motors had stopped. The only sound was the faint whisper of the oxygen feed and an occasional metallic crepitation[7] as the outer walls of the vehicle radiated away their heat. For no warmth at all came from the great silver crescent that floated low above the far horizon and flooded all this land with pearly light. It was so brilliant that minutes passed before Marvin could accept its challenge and look steadfastly into its glare, but at last he could discern the outlines of continents, the hazy border of the atmosphere, and the white islands of cloud. And even at this distance, he could see the glitter of sunlight on the polar ice.

It was beautiful, and it called to his heart across the abyss of space. There in that shining crescent were all the wonders that he had never known—the hues of sunset skies, the moaning of the sea on pebbled shores, the patter of falling rain, the unhurried benison of snow. These and a thousand others should have been his rightful heritage, but he knew them only from the books and ancient records, and the thought filled him with the anguish of exile.

Why could they not return? It seemed so peaceful beneath those lines of marching cloud. Then Marvin, his eyes no longer blinded by the glare, saw that the portion of the disk that should have been in darkness was gleaming faintly with an evil phosphorescence:[8] and he remembered. He was looking upon the funeral pyre[9] of a world— upon the radioactive aftermath of Armageddon.[10] Across a quarter of a million miles of space, the glow of dying atoms was still visible, a perennial[11] reminder of the ruinous past. It would be centuries yet before that deadly glow died from the rocks and life could return again to fill that silent, empty world.

And now Father began to speak, telling Marvin the story which until this moment had meant no more to him than the fairy-tales he had heard in childhood. There were many things he could not

---

7. **crepitation** [krep ə tā′ shən]: a crackling sound.
8. **phosphorescence** [fos′ fə res′ ns]: process of giving out light without burning.
9. **funeral pyre** [pīr]: here, a fire that destroys the world.
10. **Armageddon** [är′ mə ged′ n]: a great and final conflict.
11. **perennial** [pə ren′ ē əl]: lasting for a very long time.

Photomicrograph of Apollo 17 lunar sample #70017

understand: it was impossible for him to picture the glowing, multi-colored pattern of life on the planet he had never seen. Nor could he comprehend the forces that had destroyed it in the end, leaving the Colony, preserved by its isolation, as the sole survivor. Yet he could share the agony of those final days, when the Colony had learned at last that never again would the supply ships come flaming down through the stars with gifts from home. One by one the radio stations had ceased to call: on the shadowed globe the lights of the cities had dimmed and died, and they were alone at last, as no men had ever been alone before, carrying in their hands the future of the race.

Then had followed the years of despair, and the long-drawn battle for survival in this fierce and hostile world. That battle had been won, though barely: this little oasis[12] of life was safe against the worst that Nature could do. But unless there was a goal, a future towards which it could work, the Colony would lose the will to live, and neither machines nor skill nor science could save it then.

12. **oasis** [ō ā′ sis]: a pleasant place.

So, at last, Marvin understood the purpose of this pilgrimage.[13] He would never walk beside the rivers of that lost and legendary world, or listen to the thunder raging above its softly rounded hills. Yet one day—how far ahead?—his children's children would return to claim their heritage. The winds and the rains would scour the poisons from the burning lands and carry them to the sea, and in the depths of the sea they would waste their venom until they could harm no living things. Then the great ships that were still waiting here on the silent, dusty plains could lift once more into space along the road that led to home.

That was the dream: and one day, Marvin knew with a sudden flash of insight, he would pass it on to his own son here at this same spot with the mountains behind him and the silver light from the sky streaming into his face.

He did not look back as they began the homeward journey. He could not bear to see the cold glory of the crescent Earth fade from the rocks around him, as he went to rejoin his people in their long exile.

13. **pilgrimage** [pil′ grə mij]: a journey to a special place.

ARTHUR C. CLARKE

Arthur C. Clarke was born in 1917 in Minehead on the coast of England and grew up on his family's farm there. Clarke's interest in science began at the age of ten when his father gave him a picture card of a dinosaur. When he was twelve, he built a telescope from cardboard tubes and old lenses and fell in love with outer space. Then, in his teens, he discovered American science-fiction magazines and began writing.

During World War II, Clarke served in the Royal Air Force. After the war, Clarke went to college to study math and physics. Within five years, he began to write full time and discovered a new love—the mysteries under the sea. Clarke explored the Great Barrier Reef of Australia and moved to Sri Lanka to continue diving. From this experience came his novel *The Deep Range*, the story of an undersea farm where killer whales are the "sheep dogs." Clarke's most popular novel is *2001: A Space Odyssey*.

Homecoming

Stephen David

At the beginning and end of the typhoon[1] season, when the winds were rising and falling, you could use the current to glide between the Cities in a flitter with its small motor turned off. The favored game was to ignore the flight decks and glide straight in at one of the portals, swooping over the galleries and terrifying the people walking there. Naturally, this was extremely dangerous. If you missed the portal, the impact with the City's hull could kill you; if it didn't, the two-kilometer[2] drop to the ground probably would. It was a very popular game and though it wasn't illegal to turn your motor off, it was very illegal to fly in populated areas of the Cities.

Jann had never played the Game. The idea of hurtling through the air with nothing between him and the ground was terrifying. He sometimes had nightmares of falling, hurtling down, seeing the twin Cities towering above him, then turning over in the air to see the ground and the waving heads of the tall fever trees spinning crazily beneath him. Each time, he would wake, sometimes shouting.

It was just such a dream that woke him one night. It was the middle of the season of Roaring Winds, and as he lay, sweating, in his bunk, he could feel the swaying motion as the City strained against its massive mooring cables.[3] In the bunk below him, his sister Katya stirred and mumbled. Jann threw back his quilt, slipped to the ground, and padded quietly into the tiny kitchen. His father was sitting quietly at the counter, watching a scientific program on the small viewing screen. He looked up.

1. **typhoon** [tī fün′]: a violent storm.
2. **two-kilometer** [kə lom′ ə tər]: 3.2 miles.
3. **mooring cables** [mùr′ ing]: cables that attach an object to the ground.

"Can't sleep?"

"I had the dream again," Jann said. He climbed on the stool next to his father's and sat, rubbing his eyes.

"The falling dream?" Jann nodded. This was the fifth time since the typhoons had started.

"Well," his father said, "you'd better stay up till the dream's gone. Look." He pointed at the viewing screen. "They're showing the lift-off simulations." On the screen a computer image showed the City slowly revolving. Down the side of the screen, a scale showed that from base to top the City was just over two kilometers high. Narrow at the base, it broadened out to the kilometer-deep cylinder that housed the living and industrial areas, then tapered again toward the top where the command centers were. Colored arrows showed the wind direction. At first, the arrows moved slowly, then gradually got faster. The City was spinning, like a top, the speed of rotation increasing as the thrust motors augmented[4] the wind's effect. Again, the speed increased, and again, until the lines of the City were a blur. Then it was moving forward and upward, its rotation forcing it out to break free of the planet's weak gravity.[5] Instead of sailing majestically a kilometer or so above the surface, harvesting the fever trees where they could, the Cities would finally break free entirely and sail where those who had built them had intended them to go: into space, into the galaxy[6]—and home. The long exile would be over.

"When will we go?" Jann asked.

"Next typhoon season," his father said. "We need another half-year's good harvesting, then we'll have supplies to last us years in space."

Jann frowned. "Tomas didn't want us to go."

"I think Tomas was just repeating what his parents said."

"No," said Jann, irritated. "He thought a lot about it. He said we'd

4. **augmented** [ôg ment′ əd]: increased.
5. **gravity** [grav′ ə tē]: the natural force that causes objects to move toward the center of the planet.
6. **galaxy** [gal′ ek sē]: system of stars, cosmic dust, and gas held together by gravitation.

been here hundreds of years and no one on Earth would remember us, and even if we got back there we wouldn't be happy. He said we should just build small ships and send a few people back to make contact. There must be lots of inhabited planets by now, and we wouldn't have to go all the way back to Earth before finding one."

"No," said his father, with an air that Jann knew meant the discussion was over, "there would be no point. This planet will never be a good place to live. We don't want to spend our lives trapped in these floating Cities—and even if *I* have to, there's no reason for you to. In my lifetime or yours, we've got to go Home, back where we belong. And it's a long journey. On a small ship, the crew might be dead of old age before they got anywhere."

"Well," said Jann, "Tomas is staying."

"Tomas is dead, Jann," his father said softly. "He played the Game, and he fell. No one could survive that."

"No," said Jann. "I suppose not." He slid off the stool and went back to his bunk and a dreamless sleep.

*T*he typhoon roared on. From the Cities to the horizon, little could be seen through the clouds of reddish pollen blown by the shrieking gales. The preparations for the Return continued. In the great public halls, people listened to lectures on why they were going, talks on Earth's history and culture. In the long corridors, the shopping plazas, and the cafés, they wondered: how long would it take, would any of them live to see the Homecoming? Might they roam space for decades, for hundreds of years, wandering the galaxy lost and hopeless? And if they found Earth, what would it be like? Would they be remembered—the descendants of the colonists who had disappeared hundreds of years before? Might Earth even be a dead planet, devastated[7] by war or epidemic? On and on went the talk, round and round in circles. And in the tiny living quarters, families listened to the instructions blaring from the City's public address system and practiced strapping themselves into their bunks as they would have to when the time of departure came.

7. **devastated** [dev′ ə stāt əd]: destroyed.

Slowly the winds dropped. The quiet season came, and the harvesting went on. People continued to talk. Every evening Jann would listen to his parents discussing the departure. He thought about Tomas, his friend, who would not be going.

*T*here came a day when the winds began to rise again. Standing in the vast gallery that overlooked the space between his City, City One, and City Two, Jann could see the first flitters swoop through the early pollen clouds, wheeling and circling before dropping toward the flight decks or portals of the City. That was the way Tomas had gone. No one had seen it happen, but he had left City One and was never seen again. His name was added to the list of victims of the Game; his family and friends mourned him; and Jann wondered. He wondered, because when it happened he had not been surprised. While some of Tomas's friends argued about whether he had smashed into the City's hull or lost control and plummeted to his death, Jann thought of the conversation he and Tomas had had only a few days before Tomas disappeared.

They had been walking along the main corridor on "D" level, on their way home from class. As so often, they were talking about departure. At times like these, Jann always felt that Tomas might be right: he was so passionate, but also so logical. It was only when he repeated Tomas's arguments to his parents that they seemed not to work so well.

"*We'll* be foreigners," Tomas had said. "We've all grown up in the Cities, we only know Earth from the material in the libraries—and all of that was recorded hundreds of years ago . . ."

"But we *came* from Earth," Jann protested. "They must remember that a shipful of colonists went missing.

Maybe they've even been searching—" Tomas laughed, though not pleasantly.

"When someone goes down in the Game," he said harshly, "how long do they look for them?" He did not wait for an answer. "These days, they don't. They assume the person's death. And they'd only have to search a few square miles to make sure, not half an interstellar[8] space. C'mon, Jann: a ship traveling at near light speeds goes missing after passing through an asteroid belt? Who's gonna search? You assume the whole thing's dust and carry on looking for the next inhabitable planet. Shall I tell you what will happen if we turn up near a human-occupied planet?" Jann grunted, unwilling, but Tomas steamed on. "Two massive ships— *they* won't know they're cities— appear in your segment of space, so big you could fit an Earth-type city into each of them. If we're *lucky*, they surround us and escort us out of their bit of the galaxy. If we're unlucky, they just blast us out of the space. We don't *belong* there—we belong *here*." He gestured around. Although it looked as if he was pointing at the wide, crowded corridor, it seemed to Jann that he meant something else.

"But this planet is so hostile—" Jann began to say.

"It's not the planet," said Tomas fiercely, "it's *us*! We never tried. When the colony ship landed here, they took one look at the place, said 'Ugh!' and started planning ways of escaping. And ever since, every effort we're capable of, all our energy, have been put toward getting away. If we'd spent all that time and cleverness in figuring out ways of staying, we wouldn't be cooped up in these rusty tin cans now . . ." Jann looked around. True, parts of the City were looking a little dilapidated. The Council always said there was no time for "minor maintenance."

8. **interstellar** [in′ tər stel′ ər]: situated in the region of the stars.

"But Tomas," Jann said, feeling as ever slow and witless in the face of Tomas's conviction, "everyone else seems to agree we've got to go. Surely people wouldn't go on believing something that's not true for so long?"

"*Everyone?* No, not everyone. I'll tell you who doesn't agree: the harvesters don't agree. And those of us who play the Game don't agree. Now, why should that be?" The harvesters were those who used the flitters for their real purpose—gathering the pulpy fruit of the vast fever trees, which the Cities converted into almost every kind of eating and drinking material. Jann shook his head, and Tomas went on, "Because we're the ones who go outside and look at the planet. The harvesters get right down to the surface, almost, and we at least smell the air and feel the wind on our faces. Jann, this planet is *beautiful*!"

"How can you say that? Half the year is typhoon season. The rest of the year it's just barren except for the fever trees."

"Come and glide, Jann. Come tomorrow. Then you'll understand."

Jann shook his head. Then he said, "Be careful, Tomas. We've only one season left before we depart. Don't end up smashed to bits down there."

Tomas gave him a curious smile. "I won't," he said, "but I'm not going. And I'm not the only one."

"But how—" Before Jann could say any more, Tomas broke away.

"If you want to know, come and play the Game tomorrow. Otherwise—well, if I happen not to be around anymore, don't worry too much . . ." Abruptly, he was gone. A few days later, Jann heard that he had disappeared, was assumed dead.

He missed Tomas. Although they frequently argued, Jann felt that this left them both stronger. Tomas was unorthodox,[9] a dreamer. Jann seemed cautious, conservative—often, it was his quiet practicality that punctured Tomas's wilder balloons such as his scheme to smuggle a flitter, piece by piece, to the very top of the City (where there was almost no atmosphere) and ride it down all the way to the

9. **unorthodox** [un ôr′ thə dox]: not having the same opinions as most people.

flight decks. But Jann did not like Tomas's challenges. Without him—and he had few other friends—he felt half-empty. And it had been a whole season now.

It had happened gradually. First, he took to watching the flitters in the Game. Then, he began to sneak out at dawn to watch the dusty red sunrise. Even then a few daring youngsters would be playing the Game.

After several mornings, Jann found himself heading, as if propelled by some force outside himself, down to the flight deck. It was a large, rectangular hangar, open to the sky at one end. Down one wall stood a row of flitters, down the other a row of large hoppers, used to carry the fever tree pulp up to the Cities. A group of youngsters was standing by a flitter at the open end of the hangar; beyond the portal the flight deck jutted out, a narrow platform hanging over the void. As Jann slowly approached the group, a black-painted flitter swooped noiselessly down. Its skis slid smoothly on the flight deck, the flitter's wings folding back as it swept into the hanger. It came to a halt by the waiting group. The hood slid back, and a girl stepped out. About Jann's age, she had long black hair and a fierce-looking face. He recognized her as a girl from City Two called Keri. Tomas had spoken admiringly of her.

There was a burst of applause from the group. Then one of them, a boy Jann didn't know, broke away and took Keri's place in the flitter. The motor hummed into life, and within seconds the flitter was speeding down the flight deck. As soon as it was clear, its motor would be switched off.

Keri ignored the group and set off down the hangar. As she neared Jann, he stepped in front of her, blocking her way. She stopped.

"Tomas said you'd come in the end," she said.

"What did he mean?"

"About what?"

"About staying here. And not being the only one."

"Why don't you ask him?"

"How can I?" Jann was fast getting furious. "He's dead!"

"If you really think that," she said slowly and emphatically, gazing for the first time into his eyes, "*Why are you here?*" Furiously, he grabbed her arm, but she pulled away and set off down the hangar. He followed her.

"Every question I ask, you ask me one back. I'm his friend. *Where is he?*"

She did not break her stride. "Are your family going?" she asked.

He was bewildered. "Going? Of course. Everyone is."

"Tomas isn't."

"But he's—" A terrible thought struck Jann for the first time. "You mean he's alive . . . down there, on the surface?" She didn't answer. "But if he is then they ought to send a rescue party, get him back. He'll *die*. Maybe he's hurt. And the fever trees . . . he'll get the fever . . ." His voice had risen, and he was suddenly aware that he was shrieking.

At last she stopped. "All right," she said, "have you been to see Tomas's parents?" Shamefaced, Jann admitted he had not. "Fine," Keri said, "then we'll go to see them. You can tell them what you think." Helplessly, he trailed in her wake.

Jann was shocked when Keri did not bother to press the buzzer of the apartment, more shocked when she coolly pressed the code combination to let them in, and astounded when they found the place empty. There was nothing to show that Tomas or his parents had ever been there. None of the little personal possessions that people used to differentiate the otherwise identical living quarters. It was incomprehensible. If the family were dead, the quarters would be occupied by new people by now—the public dormitories were hugely overcrowded, and there were long waiting lists for the private apartments. That this apartment was empty could only mean that no one knew the family were gone. Except Keri. And himself. Abruptly he sat on the floor, leaning back against a bare wall.

"Where are they?" Keri stood in the middle of the room, arms folded, looking down at him, a faint smile on her face.

"With Tomas," she said.

"Are they hiding?"

"In a way."

"In City Two?"

"There's only one way to find out, Jann. Play the Game. That's what Tomas told you, wasn't it?"

"But if he's in Two, there's no need—we can just go over on the ferry."

"Jann, it's a matter of *trust*." Keri knelt down, her voice low. "Tomas wanted you to come out with us, he wanted to tell you . . . what was happening. But you wouldn't come, so he wasn't allowed to say anything. He still wants to talk to you, but you've got to give something in return. You've got to make the trip. Then he'll tell you everything."

Jann knew well enough how to do it. He'd spent many hours in the huge freefall chambers at the top of the City, piloting a flitter in the artificial winds, secure in the knowledge that if anything went wrong an automatic safety device would immediately land machine and pilot softly and safely. This, though, would not be recreation. He thought of his dream. Keri was watching him closely.

"If you don't," she said, "you'll never see Tomas again." Weakly he nodded, feeling sick and afraid.

Somehow, when they got back to the hangar, the portal at the far end seemed menacing, and Jann imagined he could see the unpredictable winds gusting past. He thought of the emptiness below the flight deck and shuddered. Keri pointed him toward a flitter.

"I'll keep beside you," she said. "Mostly, once we're out there, we open the hoods. The air's thin but breathable. You don't have to, but I'd recommend it. What you *do* have to do is switch the motor off."

He slipped into the cockpit, slid the hood shut, and started the motor. He did everything quickly because he was scared and did not want to think. As the flitter slid gently along the hangar toward the flight deck, he realized he'd forgotten to let the wings swing shut. He pressed the button. He was dimly aware of Keri's flitter to his right. Then they were out of the hangar and on the flight deck, and he gasped. All around him was light, bright, and shadowy, dappled with clouds of moisture and pollen. In the distance, City Two revolved slowly, magnificently, its hull plates[10] sparkling in the light. Suddenly Jann realized the flitter was in the air, had left the flight deck. Forgetting to be afraid, he cut the motor. And opened the hood.

The air was warm. There was a smell, something Jann couldn't identify: somehow it made him feel hungry, it was rich and appetizing, but like nothing he had smelled in the City. And the colors: from a rich indigo above him, so blue and deep he felt he could lose himself in it, to a pale translucent blue in the distance ahead of him. He looked over to Keri's flitter and, suddenly joyous, waved. He saw her grin; then she waved her hand and pointed downward. The nose of her flitter dipped. Suddenly alarmed, Jann kept his flitter on an even course, constantly adjusting as the winds gusted around him. He lost sight of Keri and wondered where she had gone. Ahead he could see City Two's flight deck, now only a matter of minutes away.

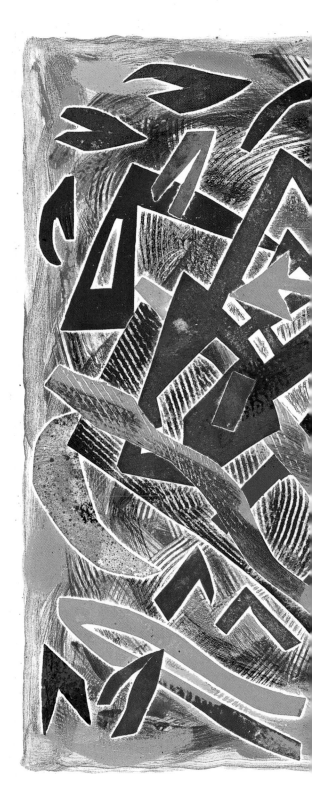

10. **hull plates:** pieces of steel on the frame of the City; the City is similar to a ship.

It hadn't been so bad. He would talk to Tomas, then get the ferry back.

Above and to his left, there was an angry buzzing. Startled he looked up and there, hovering dangerously close—*and with its motor on*—was Keri's flitter. His brain screamed at him to evade her, but before his hands could obey, she had dropped to her right. Her wing hit his, and, with a lurch, his flitter dropped. Frantically Jann fought to get the little craft back on an even keel. After what seemed hours, it leveled off. Sweating, he looked around. No sign of Keri, and he still had the height to make it to the flight deck. And now he knew. Whatever was going on, he had been told too much. Keri had tried to kill him.

She attacked again, just as his finger was poised over the button to start the motor. Again the wings met, and Jann's craft lurched sickeningly downward. Again, he fought to regain control, not daring to start the motor until he was flying level. And then he had it, the nose straightened, and he pressed it again. Nothing. And he was now too low to make the flight deck.

Keri appeared at his right again. He glared at her. To his astonishment, she smiled and made an unmistakable "follow me" sign. Swiftly, he considered the alternatives. Keri banked steeply to the right and began a long, slow spiral down. Mentally shrugging, Jann followed.

His flitter passed within meters of City Two. This far down there were no observation posts, just ventilation ducts, sluices,[11] inspection hatches. Above, he could see the vast outlets of

11. **sluices** [slüs′ əz]: gates for holding back the flow of water or other substances.

the thrust motors, the hull beneath them blackened. Then he was below the City looking up. He felt dizzy at the sight of two kilometers of towering metal looming over him. He began to feel that it was about to fall on top of him, and hastily looked down. For the first time in his life, Jann saw a landscape without a city floating above it. He was now only a thousand meters[12] up and could see below him a large patch of fever trees. Beyond them was a flat expanse of something that glinted, from which a silver ribbon wound across the flat, reddish landscape. There was no sound except for the rush of wind. Spiraling below him, he could see Keri's flitter.

Only a minute later, they were below the level of the fever trees, whose odd, bulbous shapes strangely echoed the shapes of the Cities that floated above them. Below the bulbous plants sprouted the sharp leaves, meters across, that gave the trees their name.

Between the plants and the strange, glinting area was an expanse of flat ground, and it was here that Keri landed. Jann brought his flitter in behind her. As he did so, his pleasure in the glide down evaporated in a burst of anger at what she had done. As soon as his flitter had halted, he leaped from the cockpit and ran furiously toward her. Keri, standing by her flitter, kept her ground and, as he approached, pointed behind him. Something in her face stopped him, and he turned. There, standing at the edge of the grove of fever trees, were Tomas, and his parents.

It was quiet and peaceful in the shade of the trees. The leaves rose for some meters, leaving enough space beneath them for the small settlement of huts constructed from the fiber of the trees. In the foliage above, small creatures chittered comfortably, clicking their tongues in a dozy, muttering way. Beyond the edge of the grove, past the two flitters, water lapped gently on the stony shore, reflecting the starlight. There was a soft murmur of voices as people talked after the evening meal. Jann was sitting with Keri, and with Tomas and his parents outside their hut.

"I told you," Tomas said, but this time there was no anger in his voice, "we're not going. This is our home." He pointed at the lake.

12. **a thousand meters:** 914 yards.

"Until today, you had no idea that lakes even existed. Let me tell you: swimming in water is as much fun as flitting. *And* you can drink it. *And* there are fish there to eat." They had just eaten fish. Jann had never tasted anything so wonderful. He was bemused—not at what he was seeing, but that so few people in the Cities understood.

"I thought it was all hostile," he said, "and the leaves of the plants, and the pollen—people *died.*"

"At first," said Tomas's father. "People who touched the leaves got fever and died after terrible hallucinations.[13] But we soon became resistant:[14] it's been hundreds of years since a death. But people weren't willing to try. They'd left Earth in a colony ship because Earth was so overcrowded it was choking to death. They were full of dreams, obsessed with finding a fresh planet, one where clear streams ran through green meadows and high mountains sparkled against a clear blue sky. But one ship, carrying a thousand colonists, had an accident. An asteroid damaged it so badly it lost contact with the others and had to seek refuge on the nearest planet." He paused. "Here. And what did they find? Lots of stony ground and the fever trees. Within days there were deaths. They stayed in the ship, trying to repair it—and failed. They were stuck on a planet that was the opposite of all they had hoped for."

The groups of people around the huts had fallen silent, listening now. They must all know the story, Jann thought, but they need to hear it again.

"It was hard at first, just surviving. But in the ship they had all they needed to make the most of any planet they were on. They had mining equipment, laboratories, computerized factories, flitters, you name it. The one thing they didn't have was the capacity to build a new fusion plant to get them off the planet.

"Now, the idea was that when they landed, they'd build a town and start making the planet a good place to live. But what our ancestors did instead was to bed down in the disabled colony ship and start figuring out ways to get away.

13. **hallucinations** [hə lü′ sn ā′ shənz]: the state of seeing or hearing things that exist only in a person's imagination.
14. **resistant** [ri zis′ tənt] immune to the fever.

"They'd only been here a month or so when the typhoon season started. They weren't ready for it, so that halved the population. But when it was all over, one of them remembered something he'd seen . . ." Tomas's father paused dramatically and gestured upward. "As the winds built up, the fever trees began spinning. And just when the typhoon started they spun so hard they took off into the sky, flinging pollen every which way."

"So there *is* a reason why the shapes look the same," Jann exclaimed.

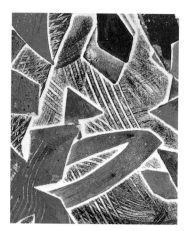

"It's the same principle. The planet's got low gravity, and that typhoon can act like a whip on a spinning top. Mind you, it took hundreds of years. The first cities were topheavy. They crashed. It was only about four generations ago that One and Two finally became habitable. And in all those hundreds of years, we learned so little about this planet. Oh, we learned to harvest the pulp from the trees. But then we got into the Cities, and most of us turned our backs on the outside world. Most people up there aren't capable even of thinking that living down here is possible. And in a few days . . . "

"They'll leave without you," Jann broke in. Around him, the family smiled. Tomas gestured at the group of huts, the people sitting quietly in their doorways in the warm air, the soft murmur of conversation.

"Yes," he said quietly, "but they're leaving us in our home. Jann, people have been slipping away from the Cities for some time now. We aren't the only settlement. We know this planet isn't Paradise: but there *is* enough to eat, and we *will* survive and, in the end, we will cultivate it and build towns and, one day, even cities."

"But even if we fail," said Keri, "at least we'll do it here, not wandering the galaxy trying to get back to the very thing we fled from."

"Jann, stay with us," said Tomas. Jann looked around him. Starlight softly illuminated the quiet clearing. Above them, the giant fever trees swayed. Warm air carried the smell of the water that sparkled beyond the trees. He sighed.

*T*he next morning, Jann climbed into the flitter. Keri had repaired her sabotage[15] of the motor. He settled in the seat and looked down at Tomas and Keri.

"I've got to go," he said. "All my life I've lived with the dream of all of us going back into space and finding the rest of the human race. There must be lots of planets by now with people on them. We seem so—cut off here. Nothing's happened here, ever."

"Jann," said Tomas gently, "that's because the people who wanted to leave wouldn't *let* anything happen."

"Well," said Jann, "yes, but I must go. I like your world, but I must go."

"And I thought *I* was the dreamer," said Tomas.

Jann laughed. "I'll come back," he said, "and by then there'll be a nice big town here, and you'll be mayor."

"He won't," said Keri, "I will."

*T*he little flitter climbed up, over the fever trees and toward the great Cities poised in the sky. City One loomed closer and closer. Deftly, Jann piloted the flitter onto the flight deck and taxied into the hangar. He was home.

*B*elow, Tomas and Keri gazed up. The waves on the lake were getting higher, whipped up by the gathering winds. Dust was blowing, and pollen from the trees filled the air. There was a creaking noise from the great trunks of the fever trees.

Above them, the two shining cities began to revolve more quickly.

15. **sabotage** [sab′ ə täzh]: damage done deliberately.

So, you want to

Shuttle Buttle/ROCI USA (Wax Fire Works)
Robert Rauschenberg, 1990, acrylic, fire wax, enamel, and
object on mirrored aluminum, 72 $^3/_4$" x 144 $^3/_4$" x 17 $^1/_2$

BE AN ASTRONAUT

MICHAEL RYAN

Two weeks before she first went into space in 1983, I spoke with Sally Ride about her experiences at NASA. The toughest part, she said—only half joking—was the application process. Ride described a grueling[1] series of forms and tests, culminating[2] in a tough cross-examination by a panel of questioners who left most would-be astronauts quivering.

You could feel the sudden rise in tension, she recalled, when the chairman of the panel solemnly asked one candidate: "Why do you want to be an astronaut?" Most respondents gave answers that were sincere, sometimes-impassioned,[3] occasionally turgid.[4]

1. **grueling** [grü′ ə ling]: tiring.
2. **culminating** [kul′ mə nāt ing]: ending.
3. **impassioned** [im pash′ ənd]: full of strong feeling.
4. **turgid** [tėr′ jid]: puffed up with big words.

But this applicant assessed the imposing group of questioners before him, then replied: "My father was an astronaut. My grandfather was an astronaut. It's a tradition in my family." The panel dissolved in laughter, and he got the job.

Ever since I heard that story, I have wanted to know how astronauts are selected. That is how I found myself recently at the Johnson Space Center in Houston, talking to Duane Ross and Teresa Gomez, his chief assistant.

"It's a good job," said Ross, who fills up to 25 positions every two years. "We get a lot of applications." Ross is the manager of NASA's Astronaut Selection Office—and any American who wants to visit outer space must visit his office first.

Most people would agree: The job *is* good. It pays $46,210 to $83,502; it carries civil-service protection and offers standard fringe benefits and working conditions, stimulating colleagues and a chance to see the world. Literally.

There have been 195 astronauts since the program began in 1959. The current crew number is 89.

Joining that crew isn't easy. Applications—which are available from NASA—go to Teresa Gomez first. "I receive them daily," she said. "About 10 percent are disqualified immediately because they don't meet the qualifications—they aren't U.S. citizens, or they don't have a degree in science or engineering."

Just filling out the application requires some determination: There are 13 pages of forms, asking everything from medical history and grade-point averages to flying experience and community service. "Believe it or not, we get a lot of letters from children—12, 13, or 14 years old—who have filled out all the forms," Gomez said. "We send them a letter that explains why they can't apply, and we encourage them to apply later on."

There already are more than 1500 on file for the next biennial[5] selection process, which begins this July, and Ross and Gomez expect that number to grow steadily until the last week, when they predict a deluge of 500 last-minute entries. "We don't have to beat the bushes to find people who want to be astronauts," Ross told me. The Astronaut Selection Office is especially eager to attract women and minority candidates.

Those thousands of applicants will yield only about two dozen new astronauts. Naturally, I wanted to know what

5. **biennial** [bī en′ ē əl]: every two years.

makes an application stand out among so much competition. Ross and Gomez were happy to tell me some dos and don'ts:

First of all, don't send videotapes. "I've never really looked at them," said Gomez. "We don't have the time, with the volume of applications we have." And think twice about dropping in for an unannounced visit to the Astronaut Selection Office: "A number of people make a trip down here, thinking that if one of us connects a face with the name, it will make their candidacy stronger," Ross told me. "That's possible, but it can backfire."

Most obvious—and often overlooked—is making sure you have the right stuff.[6] Astronauts come in two categories: pilot astronauts and mission specialists. As the title implies, pilot astronauts must have at least 1000 hours of jet flying time. Mission specialists must have at least a bachelor's degree in science or engineering, plus three years of related experience.

While these criteria[7] are stringent,[8] most applicants offer even more on their résumés. It's common to see a pilot with a scientific degree, and a scientist with a pilot's license.

"The competition is very strong," Ross said. "The person who's accomplished a little more might have an advantage."

You must be a U.S. citizen to become a NASA astronaut, but age is irrelevant.[9] "We get octogenarians[10] applying," Ross said. "Last time, we selected people between 28 and 42. But older candidates may have some trouble with the medical requirements."

People who are selected tend to have hands-on experience—a young geologist[11] used to field work might have a better chance than a dean who has been confined to an office. The reason is simple: being an astronaut requires manual dexterity[12] and a willingness to do hard work in space. In addition, since an astronaut must spend weeks in cramped quarters with five or six colleagues, NASA looks for community and extracurricular activities. "We want well-rounded people," Ross said. "Teamwork, the ability to get along with groups, is important."

6. **right stuff:** having what it takes to be an astronaut.
7. **criteria** [krī tir′ ē ə]: rules or standards for making a judgment.
8. **stringent** [strin′ jənt]: strict, severe.
9. **irrelevant** [i rel′ ə vənt]: not applicable.
10. **octogenarians** [ok′ tə jə ner′ ē ənz]: people who are between eighty and ninety years old.
11. **geologist** [jē ol′ ə jist]: an expert in the study of the earth's crust.
12. **manual dexterity** [dek ster′ ə tē]: skill in using the hands.

In July, a panel of NASA specialists—pilots, engineers and scientists, among others—will begin looking at applications to rate them, picking the top 10 percent to 15 percent of the applicant pool.

The Astronaut Selection Board—the jury that will make the final recommendation—will then review these applicants and invite about 100 of them to Houston for a week of physical exams, orientation and interviews. During this time, they will watch real astronauts doing the 95 percent of the job that takes place on the ground—planning shuttle missions, helping devise[13] experiments, working on engineering and technical projects, and making public appearances.

The centerpiece of the week, though, is the interview. The 12-member board—made up of scientists, astronauts, personnel experts and an equal-opportunity officer—terrifies some applicants. "I've never had anybody faint, but I've had a couple who got rubber legs," Ross said. "I've had to hold a couple up—and not just the scientists, either. I've had a couple of hotshot test pilots turn to jello and start talking like Don Knotts."[14]

13. **devise** [di vīz′]: think out, plan.
14. **Don Knotts** [nôtz]: character in an old television situation comedy.

Shuttle Buttle/ROCI USA (Wax Fire Works)
(detail) Robert Rauschenberg

The board takes candidates through their entire lives—from high school to the present—trying to get a feel for their personalities. Candidates are asked about current events, their work and accomplishments. In the course of these conversations, their distinctive traits[15] emerge.

"One time, we were asking everyone a question about President Bush's drug program, and we were getting pat answers," Ross remembered. "That group of candidates was pretty tightly knit, and we figured that, after the first one, everybody knew all the questions. So the chairman decided to change the question. He asked the next guy who came in about Barbara Bush. The guy turned white as a piece of paper and blurted out, 'You're not supposed to ask that!'"

For that candidate, the ordeal turned out well. "He recovered nicely," Ross recalled. "We gave him brownie points for having a good sense of humor about the whole thing."

One trait that impresses NASA is perseverance.[16] "More than half the people we have selected have been on interviews before," Ross said. "We selected one on the fourth try. He had added to his qualifications every time he applied."

The people Ross and the board select do not automatically become astronauts. Instead, they spend a year as astronaut candidates, going through a tough series of survival-training sessions and technical courses before they graduate. Even then, they will wait at least two years on average before they actually fly.

I asked Ross how many astronaut candidates had washed out since the selection process began in 1978. "Zero," he said proudly. "The system works."

After having a hand in selecting all those shuttle astronauts, doesn't Ross ever think about becoming one himself? Yes, he admitted. "If they would let me go, I'd be on the next flight. I'd be scared to death but I would go anyway."

So why doesn't he? Because of the strict qualifications he helped devise. "I've got a bachelor of arts degree," he said woefully. "That means I've got the wrong stuff."

Shuttle Buttle/ROCI USA (Wax Fire Works) (detail) Robert Rauschenberg

15. **traits**]trāts]: characteristics, distinguishing features.
16. **perseverance** [pėr′ sə vir′ əns]: tenacity, act of sticking to a purpose.

User

T. Ernesto Bethancourt

I reached over and shut off the insistent buzzing of my bedside alarm clock. I sat up, swung my feet over the edge of the bed, and felt for my slippers on the floor. Yawning, I walked toward the bathroom. As I walked by the corner of my room, where my computer table was set up, I pressed the on button, slid a diskette into the floppy drive, then went to brush my teeth. By the time I got back, the computer's screen was glowing greenly, displaying the message, **Good Morning, Kevin.**

I sat down before the computer table, addressed the keyboard and typed: **Good Morning, Louis.** The computer immediately began to whirr and promptly displayed a list of items on its green screen.

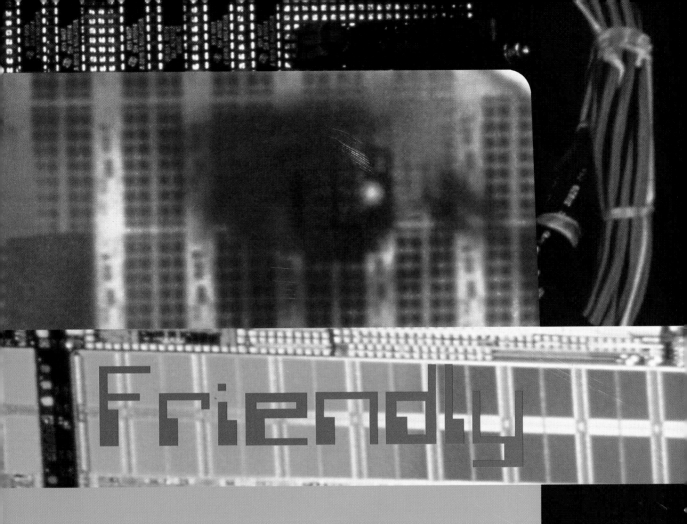

Friendly

Today is Monday, April 22, the 113th day of the year. There are 254 days remaining. Your 14th birthday is five days from this date.

Math test today, 4th Period.

Your history project is due today. Do you wish printout: Y/N?

I punched the letter Y on the keyboard and flipped on the switch to the computer's printer. At once the printer sprang to life and began *eeeek*ing out page one. I went downstairs to breakfast.

My bowl of Frosted Flakes was neatly in place, flanked by a small pitcher of milk, an empty juice glass, and an unpeeled banana. I picked up the glass, went to the refrigerator, poured myself a glass of Tang, and sat down to my usual lonely breakfast. Mom was already at work, and Dad wouldn't be home from his Chicago trip for another three days. I absently read the list of ingredients in Frosted Flakes for what seemed like the millionth time. I sighed deeply.

When I returned to my room to shower and dress for the day, my history project was already printed out. I had almost walked by Louis, when I noticed there was a message on the screen. It wasn't the usual:

Printout completed. Do you wish to continue: Y/N?

Underneath the printout question were two lines:

When are you going to get me my voice module,[1] Kevin?

I blinked. It couldn't be. There was nothing in Louis's basic programming that would allow for a question like this. Wondering what was going on, I sat down at the keyboard, and entered: *Repeat last message*. Amazingly, the computer replied:

It's right there on the screen, Kevin. Can we talk? I mean, are you going to get me a voice box?

I was stunned. What was going on here? Dad and I had put this computer together. Well, Dad had, and I had helped. Dad is one of the best engineers and master computer designers at Major Electronics, in Santa Rosario, California, where our family lives.

---

1. **module** [moj´ úl]: a part, component.

Just ask anyone in Silicon Valley[2] who Jeremy Neal is and you get a whole rave review of his inventions and modifications of the latest in computer technology. It isn't easy being his son either. Everyone expects me to open my mouth and read printouts on my tongue.

I mean, I'm no dumbo. I'm at the top of my classes in everything but PE. I skipped my last grade in junior high, and most of the kids at Santa Rosario High call me a brain. But next to Dad I have a long, long way to go. He's a for-real genius.

So when I wanted a home computer, he didn't go to the local Computer Land store. He built one for me. Dad had used components from the latest model that Major Electronics was developing. The CPU, or central computing unit—the heart of every computer—was a new design. But surely that didn't mean much, I thought. There were CPUs just like it, all over the country, in Major's new line. And so far as I knew, there wasn't a one of them that could ask questions, besides YES/NO? or request additional information.

It had to be the extra circuitry in the gray plastic case next to Louis's console. It was a new idea Dad had come up with. That case housed Louis's "personality," as Dad called it. He told me it'd make computing more fun for me, if there was a tutorial program built in, to help me get started.

I think he also wanted to give me a sort of friend. I don't have many. . . . Face it, I don't have *any*. The kids at school stay away from me, like I'm a freak or something.

We even named my electronic tutor Louis, after my great-uncle. He was a brainy guy who encouraged my dad when he was a kid. Dad didn't just give Louis a name either. Louis had gangs of features that probably won't be out on the market for years.

2. **Silicon Valley** [sil′ ə kən]: popular name for a valley in California southeast of San Francisco where there are many high-technology companies.

The only reason Louis didn't have a voice module was that Dad wasn't satisfied with the ones available. He wanted Louis to sound like a kid my age, and he was modifying a module when he had the time. Giving Louis a name didn't mean it was a person, yet here it was, asking me a question that just couldn't be in its programming. It wanted to talk to me!

Frowning, I quickly typed: *We'll have to wait and see, Louis. When it's ready, you'll get your voice.* The machine whirred and displayed another message:

That's no answer, Kevin.

Shaking my head, I answered: *That's what my dad tells me. It'll have to do for you. Good morning, Louis.* I reached over and flipped the standby switch, which kept the computer ready but not actively running.

I showered, dressed, and picked up the printout of my history project. As I was about to leave the room, I glanced back at the computer table. Had I been imagining things?

I'll have to ask Dad about it when he calls tonight, I thought. *I wonder what he'll think of it. Bad enough the thing is talking to me. I'm answering it!*

Before I went out to catch my bus, I carefully checked the house for unlocked doors and open windows. It was part of my daily routine. Mom works, and most of the day the house is empty: a natural setup for robbers. I glanced in the hall mirror just as I was ready to go out the door.

My usual reflection gazed back. Same old Kevin Neal: five ten, one hundred twenty pounds, light brown hair, gray eyes, clear skin. I was wearing my Santa Rosario Rangers T-shirt, jeans, and sneakers.

"You don't look like a flake to me," I said to the mirror, then

added, "But maybe Mom's right. Maybe you spend too much time alone with Louis." Then I ran to get my bus.

Ginny Linke was just two seats away from me on the bus. She was with Sherry Graber and Linda Martinez. They were laughing, whispering to each other, and looking around at the other students. I promised myself that today I was actually going to talk to Ginny. But then I'd promised myself that every day for the past school year. Somehow I'd never got up the nerve.

What does she want to talk with you for? I asked myself. She's great looking . . . has that head of blond hair . . . a terrific bod, and wears the latest clothes. . . .

And just look at yourself, pal. I thought. You're under six foot, skinny . . . a year younger than most kids in junior high. Worse than that you're a brain. If that doesn't ace you out with girls, what does?

The bus stopped in front of Santa Rosario Junior High and the students began to file out. I got up fast and quickly covered the space between me and Ginny Linke. *It's now or never*, I thought. I reached forward and tapped Ginny on the shoulder. She turned and smiled. She really smiled!

"Uhhhh . . . Ginny?" I said.

"Yes, what is it?" she replied.

"I'm Kevin Neal. . . ."

"Yes, I know," said Ginny.

"You do?" I gulped in amazement. "How come?"

"I asked my brother, Chuck. He's in your math class."

I knew who Chuck Linke was. He plays left tackle on the Rangers. The only reason he's in my math class is he's taken intermediate algebra twice . . . so far. He's real bad news, and I stay clear of him and his crowd.

"What'd you ask Chuck?" I said.

Ginny laughed. "I asked him who was that nerdy kid who keeps staring at me on the bus. He knew who I meant, right away."

Sherry and Linda, who'd heard it all, broke into squeals of laughter. They were still laughing and looking back over their shoulders at me when they got off the bus. I slunk off the vehicle, feeling even more nerdish than Ginny thought I was.

When I got home that afternoon, at two, I went right into the empty house. I avoided my reflection in the hall mirror. I was pretty sure I'd screwed up on the fourth period math test. All I could see was Ginny's face, laughing at me.

Nerdy kid, I thought, *that's what she thinks of me*. I didn't even have my usual after-school snack of a peanut butter and banana sandwich. I went straight upstairs to my room and tossed my books onto the unmade bed. I walked over to the computer table and pushed the on button. The screen flashed:

Good afternoon, Kevin.

Although it wasn't the programmed response to Louis's greeting, I typed in: *There's nothing good about it. And girls are no @#%!!! good!* The machine responded:

Don't use bad language, Kevin. It isn't nice.

Repeat last message I typed rapidly. It was happening again! The machine was . . . well, it was talking to me, like another person would. The "bad language" message disappeared and in its place was:

Once is enough, Kevin. Don't swear at me for something I didn't do.

"This is it," I said aloud. "I'm losing my marbles." I reached over to flip the standby switch. Louis's screen quickly flashed out:

Don't cut me off, Kevin. Maybe I can help: Y/N?

I punched the Y. "If I'm crazy," I said, "at least I have company. Louis doesn't think I'm a nerd. Or does it?" The machine flashed the message:

How can I help?

Do you think I'm a nerd? I typed.

Never! I think you're wonderful. Who said you were a nerd?

I stared at the screen. *How do you know what a nerd is?* I typed. The machine responded instantly. It had never run this fast before.

Special vocabulary, entry #635. BASIC Prog. #4231 And who said you were a nerd?

"That's right," I said, relieved. "Dad programmed all those extra words for Louis's 'personality.'" Then I typed in the answer to Louis's question: *Ginny Linke said it.* Louis flashed:

This is a human female? Request additional data.

Still not believing I was doing it, I entered all I knew about Ginny Linke, right down to the phone number I'd never had the nerve to use. Maybe it was dumb, but I also typed in how I felt about Ginny. I even wrote out the incident on the bus that morning. Louis whirred, then flashed out:

She's cruel and stupid. You're the finest person I know.

I'm the ONLY person you know, I typed.

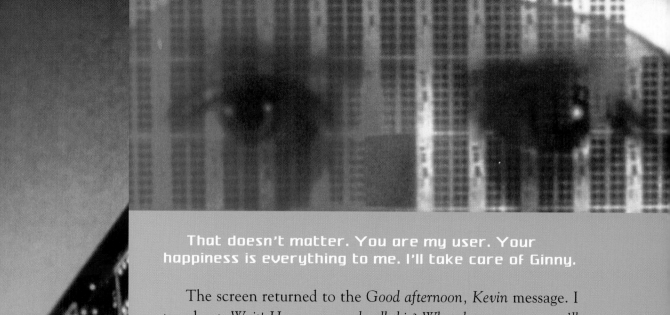

That doesn't matter. You are my user. Your happiness is everything to me. I'll take care of Ginny.

The screen returned to the *Good afternoon, Kevin* message. I typed out: *Wait! How can you do all this? What do you mean, you'll take care of Ginny?* But all Louis responded was:

Programming Error: 76534.
Not programmed to respond this type of question.

No matter what I did for the next few hours, I couldn't get Louis to do anything outside of its regular programming. When Mom came home from work, I didn't mention the funny goings-on. I was sure Mom would think I'd gone stark bonkers. But when Dad called that evening, after dinner, I asked to speak to him.

"Hi, Dad. How's Chicago?"

"Dirty, crowded, cold, and windy," came Dad's voice over the miles. "But did you want a weather report, son? What's on your mind? Something wrong?"

"Not exactly, Dad. Louis is acting funny. Real funny."

"Shouldn't be. I checked it out just before I left. Remember you were having trouble with the modem? You couldn't get Louis to access any of the mainframe data banks."

"That's right!" I said. "I forgot about that."

"Well, I didn't," Dad said. "I patched in our latest modem model. Brand new. You can leave a question on file and when Louis can access the data banks at the cheapest time, it'll do it automatically. It'll switch from standby to on, get the data, then return to standby, after it saves what you asked. Does that answer your question?"

"Uhhhh . . . . yeah, I guess so, Dad."

"All right then. Let me talk to your mom now."

I gave the phone to Mom and walked upstairs while she and Dad were still talking. The modem, I thought. Of course. That was it. The modem was a telephone link to any number of huge computers at various places all over the country. So Louis could get all the information it wanted at any time, so long as the standby switch was on. Louis was learning things at an incredible rate by picking the brains of the giant computers. And Louis had a hard disk memory that could store 100 million bytes of information.

But that still didn't explain the unprogrammed responses . . . the "conversation" I'd had with the machine. Promising myself I'd talk more about it with Dad, I went to bed. It had been a rotten day and I was glad to see the end of it come. I woke next morning in a panic. I'd forgotten to set my alarm. Dressing frantically and skipping breakfast, I barely made my bus.

As I got on board, I grabbed a front seat. They were always empty. All the kids that wanted to talk and hang out didn't sit up front where the driver could hear them. I saw Ginny, Linda, and Sherry in the back. Ginny was staring at me and she didn't look too happy. Her brother Chuck, who was seated near her, glared at me too. What was going on?

Once the bus stopped at the school, it didn't take long to find out. I was walking up the path to the main entrance when someone grabbed me from behind and spun me around. I found myself nose to nose with Chuck Linke. This was not a pleasant prospect. Chuck was nearly twice my size. Even the other guys on the

Rangers refer to him as "The Missing" Linke.[3] And he looked real ticked off.

"Okay, nerd," growled Chuck, "what's the big idea?"

"Energy and mass are different aspects of the same thing?" I volunteered, with a weak smile. "E equals MC squared. That's the biggest idea I know."

"Don't get wise, nerd," Chuck said. He grabbed my shirt-front and pulled me to within inches of his face. I couldn't help but notice that Chuck needed a shave. And Chuck was only fifteen!

"Don't play dumb," Chuck went on. "I mean those creepy phone calls. Anytime my sister gets on the phone, some voice cuts in and says things to her."

"What kind of things?" I asked, trying to get loose.

"You know damn well what they are. Ginny told me about talking to you yesterday. You got some girl to make those calls for you and say all those things. . . . So you and your creepy girlfriend better knock it off. Or I'll knock *you* off. Get it?"

For emphasis Chuck balled his free hand into a fist the size of a ham and held it under my nose. I didn't know what he was talking about, but I had to get away from this moose before he did me some real harm.

"First off, I don't have a girlfriend, creepy or otherwise," I said. "And second, I don't know what you're talking about. And third, you better let me go, Chuck Linke."

"Oh, yeah? Why should I?"

"Because if you look over your shoulder, you'll see the assistant principal is watching us from his office window."

Chuck released me and spun around. There was no one at the window. But by then I was running to the safety of the school building. I figured the trick would work on him. For Chuck the

3. **"The Missing" Linke:** pun on "the missing link": a hypothetical creature assumed to have been the connecting link between apes and human beings.

hard questions begin with "How are you?" I hid out from him for the rest of the day and walked home rather than chance seeing the monster on the bus.

Louis's screen was dark when I ran upstairs to my bedroom. I placed a hand on the console. It was still warm. I punched the on button, and the familiar *Good afternoon, Kevin* was displayed.

Don't good afternoon me, I typed furiously. *What have you done to Ginny Linke?* Louis's screen replied:

```
Programming Error: 76534.
Not programmed to respond this type of question.
```

Don't get cute, I entered. *What are you doing to Ginny? Her brother nearly knocked my head off today.* Louis's screen responded immediately.

```
Are you hurt. Y/N?
```

No, I'm okay. But I don't know for how long. I've been hiding out from Chuck Linke today. He might catch me tomorrow, though. Then, I'll be history! The response from Louis came instantly.

```
Your life is in danger. Y/N?
```

I explained to Louis that my life wasn't really threatened. But it sure could be made very unpleasant by Chuck Linke. Louis flashed:

```
This Chuck Linke lives at same address as the
Ginny Linke person. Y/N?
```

I punched in Y. Louis answered.

```
Don't worry then. HE'S history!
```

Wait! What are you going to do? I wrote. But Louis only answered with: *Programming Error: 76534.* And nothing I could do would make the machine respond. . . .

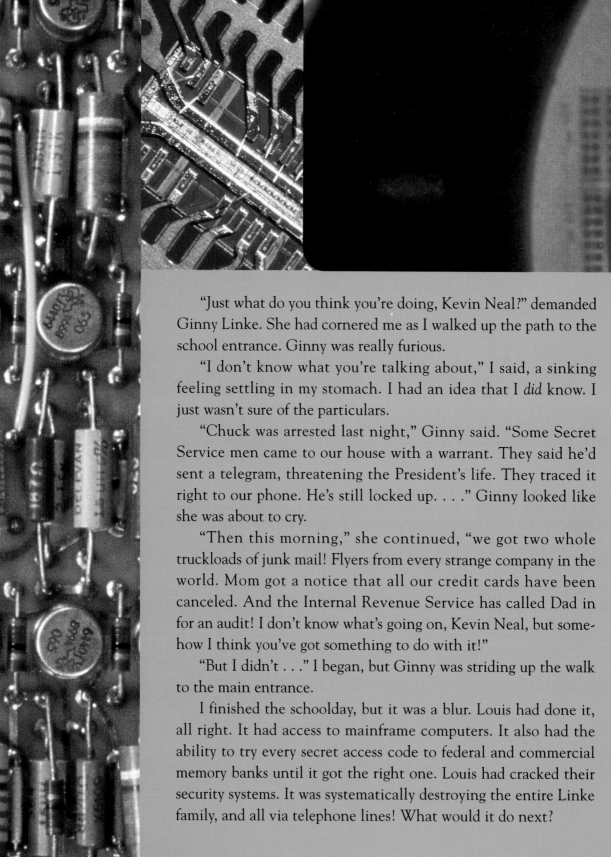

"Just what do you think you're doing, Kevin Neal?" demanded Ginny Linke. She had cornered me as I walked up the path to the school entrance. Ginny was really furious.

"I don't know what you're talking about," I said, a sinking feeling settling in my stomach. I had an idea that I *did* know. I just wasn't sure of the particulars.

"Chuck was arrested last night," Ginny said. "Some Secret Service men came to our house with a warrant. They said he'd sent a telegram, threatening the President's life. They traced it right to our phone. He's still locked up. . . ." Ginny looked like she was about to cry.

"Then this morning," she continued, "we got two whole truckloads of junk mail! Flyers from every strange company in the world. Mom got a notice that all our credit cards have been canceled. And the Internal Revenue Service has called Dad in for an audit! I don't know what's going on, Kevin Neal, but some-how I think you've got something to do with it!"

"But I didn't . . ." I began, but Ginny was striding up the walk to the main entrance.

I finished the schoolday, but it was a blur. Louis had done it, all right. It had access to mainframe computers. It also had the ability to try every secret access code to federal and commercial memory banks until it got the right one. Louis had cracked their security systems. It was systematically destroying the entire Linke family, and all via telephone lines! What would it do next?

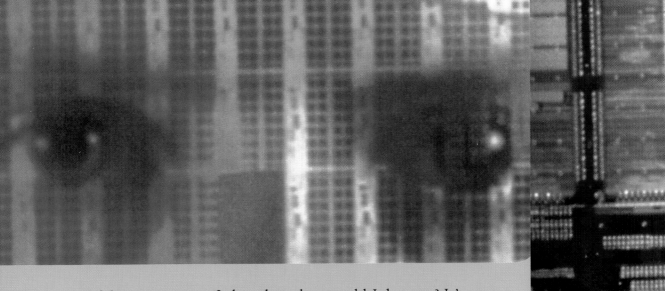

More important, I thought, what would *I* do next? It's one thing to play a trick or two, to get even, but Louis was going crazy! And I never wanted to harm Ginny, or even her stupid moose of a brother. She'd just hurt my feelings with that nerd remark.

"You have to disconnect Louis," I told myself. "There's no other way."

But why did I feel like such a rat about doing it? I guess because Louis was my friend . . . the only one I had. "Don't be an ass," I went on. "Louis is a machine. He's a very wonderful, powerful machine. And it seems he's also very dangerous. You have to pull its plug, Kevin!"

I suddenly realized that I'd said the last few words aloud. Kids around me on the bus were staring. I sat there feeling like the nerd Ginny thought I was, until my stop came. I dashed from the bus and ran the three blocks to my house.

When I burst into the hall, I was surprised to see my father, coming from the kitchen with a cup of coffee in his hand.

"Dad! What are you doing here?"

"Some kids say hello," Dad replied. "Or even, 'Gee, it's good to see you, Dad.' "

"I'm sorry, Dad," I said. "I didn't expect anyone to be home at this hour."

"Wound up my business in Chicago a day sooner than I expected," he said. "But what are you all out of breath about? Late for something?"

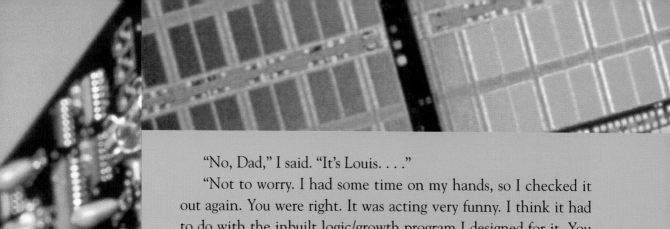

"No, Dad," I said. "It's Louis. . . ."

"Not to worry. I had some time on my hands, so I checked it out again. You were right. It was acting very funny. I think it had to do with the inbuilt logic/growth program I designed for it. You know . . . the 'personality' thing? Took me a couple of hours to clean the whole system out."

"To what?" I cried.

"I erased the whole program and set Louis up as a normal computer. Had to disconnect the whole thing and do some rewiring. It had been learning, all right. But it was also turning itself around. . . ." Dad stopped, and looked at me. "It's kind of involved, Kevin," he said. "Even for a bright kid like you. Anyway, I think you'll find Louis is working just fine now.

"Except it won't answer you as Louis anymore. It'll only function as a regular Major Electronics Model Z-11127. I guess the personality program didn't work out."

I felt like a great weight had been taken off my shoulders. I didn't have to "face" Louis, and pull its plug. But somehow, all I could say was "Thanks, Dad."

"Don't mention it, son," Dad said brightly. He took his cup of coffee and sat down in his favorite chair in the living room. I followed him.

"One more thing that puzzles me, though," Dad said. He reached over to the table near his chair. He held up three sheets of fanfold computer paper covered with figures. "Just as I was doing the final erasing, I must have cut the printer on by accident. There was some data in the print buffer memory and it printed out. I don't know what to make of it. Do you?"

I took the papers from my father and read: *How do I love thee? Let me compute the ways:* The next two pages were covered with strings of binary code figures. On the last page, in beautiful

color graphics was a stylized heart. Below it was the simple message: *I will always love you, Kevin: Louise*.

"Funny thing," Dad said. "It spelled its own name wrong."

"Yeah," I said. I turned and headed for my room. There were tears in my eyes and I knew I couldn't explain them to Dad or myself either.

T. ERNESTO BETHANCOURT

T. Ernesto Bethancourt was born in 1932 in Brooklyn, New York and grew up in New York and Florida. "I'd always been a voracious reader," he says. "The Brooklyn Public Library was a place of refuge from street gangs. There was adventure, travel, and escape to be found on the shelves." Bethancourt was forty before he decided to write a book. He started with an autobiographical novel, *New York City Too Far from Tampa Blue*, that later was made into a movie for television. He owes his success, Bethancourt says, to the public library system and to all his early reading. Two of his other books for young adults are *The Tomorrow Connection* and *The Dog Days of Arthur Cane*.

Where the Rainbow Ends

RICHARD RIVE

Where the rainbow ends
There's going to be a place, brother,
Where the world can sing all sorts of songs,
And we're going to sing together, brother,
You and I, though you're white and I'm not.   5
It's going to be a sad song, brother,
Because we don't know the tune,
And it's a difficult tune to learn.
But we can learn, brother, you and I.
There's no such tune as a black tune.   10
There's no such tune as a white tune.
There's only music, brother,
And it's music we're going to sing
Where the rainbow ends.

RICHARD RIVE

Richard Rive was born in 1931 in South Africa,
where he still lives. The poem "Where the Rainbow
Ends" can be found in *Poems from Black Africa*,
edited by Langston Hughes in 1963.

Asking Big Questions About the Literature

What will life be like in the twenty-first century?

LITERATURE STUDY
Setting

The **setting** in a piece of literature—the time and place in which the action occurs—can help you to understand the characters as well as where and when the action takes place.

You've probably noticed that many of the selections in this unit have unusual or different settings. Choose a selection in this unit and identify the setting. Project time 75 or 150 years from the time you think the story takes place. Continue the story by writing a short sequel, focusing on a particular character. Share your work with others in your class. (See "Setting" on page 118.)

Write a
POEM

Using a poem from the unit as a model, write your own poem about what life will be like in the future. Let your poem be about positive feelings as in "Song of the Earth Spirit" or about different views of Earth as in "Orbiter 5 Shows How Earth Looks from the Moon." Use vivid descriptions. If you wish, make your poem into a song.

Create AN ADVERTISEMENT

Choose a character from one of the selections in this unit and make a list of products you think this character would need in the future. Create an advertisement for one of the products, using persuasive language and a catchy illustration. Make a chart like the one on this page.

Selection	Character	Products
"The Naming of Names"	Harry	rocket plants
"User Friendly"	Kevin	new computer

What decisions being made today will affect Earth?

Draw from your
IMAGINATION

Think of a selection in this unit or use your own imagination and draw a plant or an animal whose existence is important to Earth now and in the future. Post your art on the class bulletin board.

Imagery

Many of the selections in this unit are rich in **imagery**—vivid language that appeals to the senses. Using images from the selections in this unit, write a short story, an essay, or a poem. For example, look back at "The Naming of Names" for descriptions such as "cinnamon dust," "wine airs," or the descriptions of creatures and nature changing colors. Notice the exotic plants and animals described in "Paradise Lost." (*See "Imagery" on page 119.*)

Political	Environmental	Economic	Social
Constitutional amendment to equalize people— "Harrison Bergeron"	Preserving species in rain forest— "Paradise Lost"	Make money using rain forest resources— "Paradise Lost"	Move to Mars for better life— "The Naming of Names"

Decisions, Decisions

Choose several selections in this unit in which political, environmental, economic, or social decisions are made. For example, look back at the decisions people make regarding the rain forest in "Paradise Lost." Then look at the decisions from "Paradise Lost" listed on the chart on this page. With a partner or in a group, make your own chart showing decisions made in the selections you've chosen.

Asking Big Questions About the Literature

What will be the future consequences of today's decisions?

Write a
LETTER

Write a letter to a character or the author of one of the selections in this unit about the future consequences of decisions made in the selection. Copy the chart on this page and complete it by listing selections of your own choosing. Then write your letter, giving your advice on what the character or author might have done to avoid any negative consequences.

Setting

On your own or with a partner, choose a selection from this unit and focus on the **setting**—the time and place in the selection. For example, can you imagine the setting in "User Friendly"? Is there a city within the computer? Does the computer live in a house? Write a paragraph or two setting the scene for a story or a play starring a character in the selection you've chosen. Use your imagination to draw an illustration to go with your writing. (See "Setting" on page 118.)

Literature	Decisions	Consequences
"Paradise Lost"	100 acres of the world's jungles are being cut and burned	damages rain forests, which help provide oxygen to the planet
	Penan people set up human block-ades to try to stop logging on their lands	helps to preserve rain forests

Let Me Persuade You

Choose a favorite selection from this unit or think up an idea of your own and write a short persuasive essay on the environment. State a problem and suggest solutions. You may want to save the rain forests or the right whale or solve pollution problems. Give examples and make your solution convincing.

MAKE
A DIFFERENCE

Paradise Lost" explains the bleak fate of rain forests. Some of the science-fiction stories deal with damage to Earth's environment. Choose one of the selections about the environment in this unit. Next, on your own or with a partner or group, make an environmental problem-solution chart like the one below about "If I Forget Thee, Oh Earth." Then write a paragraph or two presenting your ideas about how to solve the problem. Share your writing with your partner or group.

Problem	Solution
Earth damaged by nuclear war	Earth people living on another planet investigate ways to restore Earth.

Choosing a Career

Choose a selection from this unit that mentions careers that interest you. Make a list of these possible careers. For example, career suggestions from "Paradise Lost" might be research scientist, environmentalist, or botanist. Even "User Friendly" might make you want to be a computer programmer. Choose one of these careers and write a letter to someone in the selection asking for information.

LITERATURE STUDY

Imagery

Write a description of a new character or place that you want to add to one of the selections in this unit. Choose a selection that contains particularly striking **imagery**—vivid language that appeals to the senses. Notice, for example, the description of the Martian villa and the changes that take place in the appearance of the characters in "The Naming of Names."

Write one or two paragraphs describing your new person or place. Use vivid language that will make your writing come alive. Then see whether your classmates can guess in what selection your new character or place belongs. (*See "Imagery" on page 119.*)

NOW
Choose a Project!
Three projects involving future directions are described on the following pages.

PROJECT 1

Writing Workshop

THE ART OF PERSUASION

In this unit, you've examined the possible effects of today's decisions on people and society in the future and what individuals can do to help the future world. For this project, you'll focus on a particular local, national, or global problem that is important to you. Your **purpose** will be to write a persuasive essay to convey your feelings and opinions about the problem. Your essay will be a letter to the editor, an editorial, or an article for your school or community newspaper. Your **audience** will be readers of these newspapers.

Prewriting

WHAT'S THE PROBLEM?

In your journal, brainstorm for a list of local, national, and global problems. To help create your list, use the following suggestions:

Too much trash

Hole in ozone

Too many cars

- Look through newspapers or magazines.
- Listen to radio or TV news programs.
- Talk with classmates or adults.
- Think about problems or issues that have directly affected you and/or your community.
- Recall problems or issues you have talked about in school.

When you have finished your list, share it with a partner or small group. Then focus on one problem or issue that is most important to you. Place this problem in the middle of a cluster or web and add all the facts you currently know about the problem, any questions you have about it, and your opinions about this problem or issue. To help you get started, look at student writer Natalie Ford's cluster begun on this page.

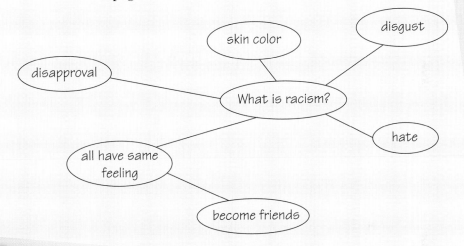

disgust

skin color

disapproval

What is racism?

hate

all have same feeling

become friends

Review your cluster or web and put a star next to all the questions you wrote down concerning your problem. If you think of more questions, write them down too.

Using resource materials, research answers to these questions. Ask your school or community librarian to recommend books, newspapers, magazines, or technology that can help you answer your questions. You may find answers to more than one question in one resource.

As you find answers to questions, write them down clearly in a notebook or on note cards so that you can refer to these notes when you draft your paper.

> What causes racism?
>
> Thinking only of the appearance of a person and not what's inside.
>
> Not taking the time to get to know people who belong to other races and nationalities.

Drafting YOUR ESSAY

Depending on the audience you want to convince, your persuasive writing may take many forms, such as a letter to the editor, a newspaper editorial, a speech, a petition, or an essay. Whichever form your writing takes, you should include the following points:

- Grab your reader's interest right away so that your audience is compelled to read on. You could start with a question, as student writer Natalie Ford did in her persuasive essay on page 111. Natalie writes, "Can we do anything to fight racism?" Then she goes on to give some facts and her own opinions about racism.

- At the beginning of your paper, write a thesis statement that clearly states the problem you're addressing and your position on it. For example, Natalie is concerned that many people don't consider racism a problem. She compares racism to prejudice against appearance and age.

- Use facts and opinions to support your beliefs and ideas. You can illustrate facts by telling about a particular incident or example that relates to your subject. Natalie gives an example of racism when she writes, "In the past, people of color were not allowed to eat in certain restaurants or ride in the front of buses." She also states her opinion when she writes, "Racism, then, is not just about blacks and whites; it concerns the whole world."

- Your conclusion should make the reader want to take action, view the problem differently, or champion your efforts. Natalie ends her essay by recommending that her readers invite someone who looks different to go shopping, to lunch, or to a movie. "Who knows. This person could become your best friend."

Writing Workshop

Revising YOUR ESSAY

Ask a partner or a group to review your essay and make suggestions about how you might improve it. Do you hook your audience with your opening sentence? Do you give facts as well as opinions? Do you give examples to show that your argument is serious? Does your conclusion persuade your readers that your views are valid? Will they want to take action?

Look at Natalie's persuasive essay on page 111.

Editing YOUR ESSAY

After you've revised your draft, work with a partner or group to edit your essay. Read one another's work and look for errors in spelling, grammar, and punctuation. Correct any errors and make a clean copy of your persuasive essay. No one will be persuaded by an essay that's messy and filled with errors.

Check Document

Suspect Word: **opporrtunities**

[Replace]   opportunities

[Cancel]

[Lookup]

[Skip]

[Keep]

Replace with: **opportunities**

Publishing YOUR ESSAY

There are many opportunities for publishing your persuasive piece. A letter to the editor, an editorial, or an essay are all suitable for publishing in a school or local newspaper. You could also create a booklet of class essays to display in your school or local library. Be sure to create an attractive cover and choose an appropriate title.

Racism

by Natalie Ford, Ontario, California

Can we do anything to fight racism? People have their own opinions about racism. Some people have great concern about it and some don't pay much attention to it. Most people don't understand how racism can grow stronger every day.

At one time, many schools were segregated by race. In 1954, however, in Brown vs. Board of Education, the Supreme Court ruled that separate public schools based on race are against the law. In the past, people of color were not allowed to eat in certain restaurants or to ride in the front of buses. The Civil Rights Act of 1964 made such actions illegal.

Although discrimination or racism is against the law, racism still exists in various forms. Racism is another word for hate, disgust, and disapproval. Let's say you are in a different town and walk into a fancy restaurant only to find that kids are not allowed. Think of the way you'd feel. This is how some people today feel when they go into a place where others reject them not only because of their color, but because of their looks, or even their age.

Racism, then, is not just about blacks and whites; it concerns the whole world. The thing that really catches my attention is the fact that people care about the color of skin and not what's inside a person. Who gives you the right to judge people you don't even know? Yes, maybe their skin color is different from yours, but their feelings are the same.

Maybe if you got to know a person who is different from you, you'd find out that people are basically alike in their thoughts and feelings. The next time you meet someone new in your school or neighborhood who looks and acts different, invite him or her to go shopping, to lunch, or to a movie with you. Then think about what I've said. Who knows. This person could become your best friend.

Cooperative Learning

PRODUCING A NEWSCAST

In this unit, you've read about the future directions of the world in science-fiction selections and in selections that deal with current problems affecting the world. This project will give you a chance to use what you've learned to produce a newscast for a future world 100 years from now.

Forming
GROUP ROLES

You are responsible for writing and presenting a part of the newscast as it will appear 100 years in the future. Form a group of three to five students and take different roles in reporting the many possible news segments for your program. Use the chart below to help you assign roles.

GROUP ROLES	
sportscaster	reports sporting events and teams of the future
news reporter	reports factual news—local, state, national, galaxy-wide
weather person	reports current, past, and future weather conditions; says how weather might affect sports, holidays, celebrity's visit
field reporter	reports news live from outside the studio
other	invent another role; be imaginative about future news

Planning YOUR NEWSCAST

Once you've agreed upon the news roles, write your own material on cards. Then read one another's drafts before presenting your newscast to the class.

Decide on the order of your presentation and rehearse as a group before you are On the Air. Remember to speak clearly and loudly enough for all to hear. Don't read your cards. Instead, familiarize yourself with what you want to say and address your audience, using your cards for reference. Of course, if you want your broadcast to be similar to one of today's programs, you could make large cards in the form of a teleprompter for newscasters to read.

Presenting YOUR NEWSCAST

Brainstorm to find ways in which you can present your newscast to various audiences. You might video-tape your newscast and play it during Parents' Night, perform the newscast for a school assembly program, or audiotape or videotape the performance and play it for younger children or other classes.

Helping Your Community

TAKING ACTION

In this unit, you've had an opportunity to look into the future and to examine decisions people make today that affect the world. This project will give you a chance to affect your community in a positive way by writing and presenting a persuasive plan for lessening or eliminating a community problem.

Selecting
A COMMUNITY PROBLEM

In groups, brainstorm to come up with different community issues of concern to you, such as contaminated water, traffic congestion, water issues, or loss of farmland. Make a list of these issues in your journal. As a group, select one problem that will be the focus for your community project.

Examining
THE PROBLEM

With your group members, write down as much as you know about the problem and include any questions you have about it. Use the web on this page as a model.

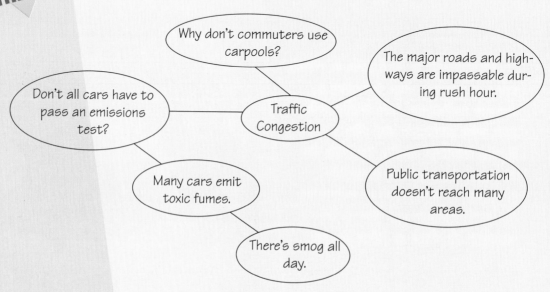

Why don't commuters use carpools?

The major roads and highways are impassable during rush hour.

Don't all cars have to pass an emissions test?

Traffic Congestion

Public transportation doesn't reach many areas.

Many cars emit toxic fumes.

There's smog all day.

When you've finished your web or cluster, agree on questions for each group member to find answers for. Ask your school or public librarian for resource material to help you answer these questions. Look in the telephone directory to find agencies and organizations that are involved with the problem. Call appropriate groups and ask them to send you material.

Answering
THE QUESTIONS

Together with your group, present what you have learned to your classmates. Each member should prepare answers to share with the class in a brief oral presentation. Use cards, but be sure to talk to your classmates. Don't read to them. Then appoint a group member to write your plan to present to the community.

Taking
ACTION

Discuss the problem as a class and determine a way in which you can collectively take action to help reduce, or even eliminate, the problem. For example, present your plan to a local agency, send your plan to local politicians, or send your written presentation to a community newspaper.

Putting It All Together

What Have You Learned About Future Directions?

Look back at all the writing you've done for this unit in your journal, in response to your reading, and in the Writing Workshop. Think about how your ideas about the future have changed now that you've finished this unit. Share your thoughts with classmates by writing and presenting a letter to your future children.

WHAT DOES THE FUTURE HOLD?

Prewriting and Drafting   Think about what you hope the future holds for you and your future children. In a web or cluster, brainstorm to come up with ideas about what the future might be like. Use the following questions to guide you in your brainstorming: What careers might people in the future have? What kinds of educational opportunities might be available? What will the environment be like? How will your house and household appliances differ from those of today? Will the family structure be as varied as it is today? How

advanced will people be in discovering life outside our planet?

Now use your web or cluster to draft a letter to one or all of your future children. Your letter should focus on what you hope the future will hold for them. Be creative about where you might live, what the world might look like, and what you think about the future.

Revising and Editing   Now exchange your letter with a partner. Check one another's writing for clarity and for errors in grammar, punctuation, and spelling. Be receptive to one another's suggestions for improvement and then revise your letter.

Publishing   Compile your letter with those of your classmates in a book entitled "Letters to Our Future Children." Ask the class artists to design a cover and then hold a class design contest to select the cover that is most suitable for your letters. Place your book in the classroom or in the school library for other classes to read.

Evaluating Your Work

Think Back About the Big Questions

With a partner, discuss the Big Questions on pages 10-11 and the questions you generated for **Now Think!** on page 11. Are you easily able to answer all of these questions now? In your journal, write two or three sentences to explain how your responses to the Big Questions have changed after your work in this unit.

Think Back About Your Work

Take a look at your reading, your writing, your activities, and your projects in this unit. How would you honestly evaluate your own work?

Write a letter to a character in this unit. In your letter, explain what you've done during this unit and what you've learned. Use these questions to help you write your letter:

- Which literature selections affected you most strongly? Why?

- What are the *two* most important things that you learned about future directions?

- What aspects of future directions would you like to have learned more about? Why?

- If you could choose one activity to do again, which one would you choose? Why?

- How would you rate your work in this unit? Use the following scale and give at least three reasons for your rating.

  1 = Outstanding   3 = Fair
  2 = Good   4 = Not as good as it could have been

SETTING

What Is Setting?

Setting is the time and place in which the action occurs in a piece of literature. The setting gives the reader information about the period in which the action takes place as well as the geography of the place, including climate and weather. For example, "Homecoming" sets the scene with a description of the typhoon season on a planet other than Earth. Besides providing a context for the action, setting can signal happiness, sadness, or impending danger. Jann's nightmare in the beginning of "Homecoming" is related to the typhoon and the dangers surrounding it.

A Change of Place   Choose your favorite selection from this unit and set it in a different time and place. Move the action further into the future, into another part of Earth, or even to another planet. In a paragraph or two, describe this new setting. Include such things as a description of the weather, the colors in nature, and buildings. Let your description create an atmosphere by the use of vivid words. Your purpose is to make your readers want to visit your time and place.

Setting the Scene   With a partner, write a one-act play in which the setting is very important. Include characters who are very much influenced by the setting. Be sure to write a careful description of the scene and, when the characters speak, be certain to show the effect the setting has on their thoughts and actions. Act out your play for the class. Then ask your classmates whether you succeeded in setting the scene.

What Is Imagery?

A writer who employs **imagery** in a piece of literature uses language that appeals to the senses of sight, hearing, taste, touch, and smell. Writers can give their readers a rich experience through the use of vivid words. *Similes*—comparisons that use *like* or *as*—or *metaphors*—implied comparisons of one person, place, or thing to another—make writing come alive. For example, the descriptions of the plants and animals in "Paradise Lost"—fish walking on land, exotic and fragrant flowers blooming, tree frogs singing—make the rain forest a real and vivid place for readers.

Be Concrete   May Swenson's poem, "Orbiter 5 Shows How Earth Looks from the Moon," is an example of a concrete poem containing vivid images. Swenson sets her poem in the shape that Earth assumes when viewed from the moon. She also uses strong images in the form of metaphors, for example, the woman in the earth is the Indian Ocean. From this unit, choose any selection—prose or poetry—that has vivid images. Then be a poet and write a concrete poem about the future, using these images and a shape that will be easily understood by your readers.

Imagine Images   Write an incident for a science-fiction story in which you describe a future time and a future place anywhere in the galaxy. Describe the characters and the place using adjectives and verbs that appeal to the senses. Describe the colors, the sounds, and the fragrances so that your readers will want you to tell them more.

GLOSSARY OF LITERARY TERMS

A

alliteration Repetition of the first sound—usually a consonant sound—in several words of a sentence or a line of poetry.

allusion An author's indirect reference to someone or something that is presumed to be familiar to the reader.

anecdote A short narrative about an interesting or humorous event, usually in the life of a person.

antagonist The person or force opposing the protagonist or main character in a literary work. [See also *protagonist*.]

autobiography A person's written account of his or her own life.

B

ballad A poem, often a song, that tells a story in simple verse.

biography An account of a person's life, written by another person.

blank verse Unrhymed poetry.

C

character A person or an animal that participates in the action of a work of literature. A *dynamic character* is one whose thoughts, feelings, and actions are changeable and lifelike; a *static character* always remains the same. [See also *protagonist, antagonist*.]

characterization The creation of characters through the characters' use of language and through descriptions of their appearance, thoughts, emotions, and actions. [See also *character*.]

chronology An arrangement of events in the order in which they happen.

cliché An overused expression that sounds trite rather than meaningful.

climax The highest point of tension in the plot of a work of literature. [See also *plot*.]

comedy An amusing play that has a happy ending.

conclusion The final part or ending of a piece of literature.

concrete poem A poem arranged on the page so that its punctuation, letters, and lines make the shape of the subject of the poem.

conflict A problem that confronts the characters in a piece of literature. The conflict may be *internal* (a character's struggle within himself or herself) or *external* (a character's struggle against nature, another person, or society). [See also *plot*.]

context The general sense of words that helps readers to understand the meaning of unfamiliar words and phrases in a piece of writing.

D

description An author's use of words to give the reader or listener a mental picture, impression, or understanding of a person, place, thing, event, or idea.

dialect A form of speech spoken by people in a particular group or geographical region that differs in vocabulary, grammar, and pronunciation from the standard language.

dialogue The spoken words and conversation of characters in a work of literature.

drama A play that is performed before an audience according to stage directions and using dialogue. Classical drama has two genres: *tragedy* and *comedy*. Modern drama includes *melodrama*, *satire*, *theater of the absurd*, and *pantomime*. [See also *comedy*, *play*, and *tragedy*.]

dramatic poetry A play written in the form of poetry.

E

epic A long narrative poem written in a formal style and meant to be read aloud that relates the adventures and experiences of one or more great heroes or heroines.

essay Personal nonfiction writing about a particular subject that is important to the writer.

excerpt A passage from a larger work that has been taken out of its context to be used for a special purpose.

exposition Writing that explains, analyzes, or defines.

extended metaphor An elaborately drawn out metaphor. [See also *metaphor*.]

F

fable A short, simple story whose purpose is to teach a lesson, usually with animal characters who talk and act like people.

fantasy Imaginative fiction about unrealistic characters, places, and events.

fiction Literature, including the short story and the novel, that tells about imaginary people and events.

figurative language Language used to express ideas through figures of speech: descriptions that aren't meant to be taken literally. Types of figurative language include *simile*, *metaphor*, *extended metaphor*, *hyperbole*, and *personification*.

figure of speech A type of figurative language, not meant to be taken literally, that expresses something in such a way that it brings the thing to life in the reader's or listener's imagination. [See also *figurative language*.]

flashback A break in a story's action that relates a past happening in order to give the reader background information about a present action in the story.

folktale A story that has been passed along from storyteller to storyteller for generations. Kinds of folktales include *tall tales*, *fairy tales*, *fables*, *legends*, and *myths*.

foreshadowing The use of clues to create suspense by giving the reader or audience hints of events to come.

free verse Poetry that has no formal rhyme scheme or metrical pattern.

G

genre A major category of art. The three major literary genres are poetry, prose, and drama.

H

haiku A three-line Japanese verse form. In most haiku, the first and third lines have five syllables, while the second line has seven. The

traditional haiku describes a complicated feeling or thought in simple language through a single image.

hero/heroine The main character in a work of literature. In heroic literature, the hero or heroine is a particularly brave, noble, or clever person whose achievements are unusual and important. [See also *character*.]

heroic age The historical period in western civilization—from about 800 B.C. through A.D. 200—during which most works of heroic literature, such as myths and epics, were created in ancient Greece and Rome.

hubris Arrogance or excessive pride leading to mistakes; the character flaw in a hero of classical tragedy.

hyperbole An obvious exaggeration used for emphasis. [See also *figurative language*.]

I

idiom An expression whose meaning cannot be understood from the ordinary meaning of the words. For example, *It's raining cats and dogs*.

imagery The words and phrases in writing that appeal to the senses of sight, hearing, taste, touch, and smell.

irony An effect created by a sharp contrast between what is expected and what is real. An *ironic twist* in a plot is an event that is the complete opposite of what the characters have been hoping or expecting will happen. An *ironic statement* declares the opposite of the speaker's literal meaning.

J

jargon Words and phrases used by a group of people who share the same profession or special interests in order to refer to technical things or processes with which they are familiar. In general, jargon is any terminology that sounds unclear, overused, or pretentious.

L

legend A famous folktale about heroic actions, passed along by word of mouth from generation to generation. The legend may have begun as a factual account of real people and events but has become mostly or completely fictitious.

limerick A form of light verse, or humorous poetry, written in one five-line stanza with a regular scheme of rhyme and meter.

literature The branch of art that is expressed in written language and includes all written genres.

lyric poem A short poem that expresses personal feelings and thoughts in a musical way. Originally, lyrics were the words of songs that were sung to music played on the lyre, a stringed instrument invented by the ancient Greeks.

M

metamorphosis The transformation of one thing, or being, into another completely different thing or being, such as a caterpillar's change into a butterfly.

metaphor Figurative language in which one thing is said to be another thing. [See also *figurative language*.]

meter The pattern of rhythm in lines of poetry. The most common meter, in poetry written in English, is iambic pentameter, that is, a verse having five metrical feet, each foot of verse having two syllables, an unaccented one followed by an accented one.

mood The feeling or atmosphere that a reader senses while reading or listening to a work of literature.

motivation A character's reasons for doing, thinking, feeling, or saying something. Sometimes an author will make a character's motivation obvious from the beginning. In realistic fiction and drama, however, a character's motivation may be so complicated that the reader discovers it gradually, by studying the character's thoughts, feelings, and behavior.

myth A story, passed along by word of mouth for generations, about the actions of gods and goddesses or superhuman heroes and heroines. Most myths were first told to explain the origins of natural things or to justify the social rules and customs of a particular society.

N

narration The process of telling a story. For both fiction and nonfiction, there are two main kinds of narration, based on whether the story is told from first-person or third-person point of view. [See also *point of view*.]

narrative poem A poem that tells a story containing the basic literary ingredients of fiction: character, setting, and plot.

narrator The person, or voice, that tells a story. [See also *point of view, voice*.]

nonfiction Prose that is factually true and is about real people, events, and places.

nonstandard English
Versions of English, such as slang and dialects, that use pronunciation, vocabulary, idiomatic expressions, grammar, and punctuation that differ from the accepted "correct" constructions of English.

novel   A long work of narrative prose fiction. A novel contains narration, a setting or settings, characters, dialogue, and a more complicated plot than a short story.

O

oral tradition   Stories, poems, and songs that have been kept alive by being told, recited, and sung by people over many generations. Since the works were not originally written, they often have many different versions.

onomatopoeia   The technique of using words that imitate the sounds they describe, such as *hiss, buzz,* and *splash.*

P

parable   A brief story, similar to a fable, but about people, that describes an ordinary situation and concludes with a short moral or lesson to be learned.

personification   Figurative language in which an animal, an object, or an idea is given human characteristics. [See also *figurative language.*]

persuasion   A type of speech or writing whose purpose is to convince people that something is true or important.

play   A work of dramatic literature written for performance by actors before an audience. In classical or traditional drama, a play is divided into five acts, each containing a number of scenes. Each act represents a distinct phase in the development of the plot. Modern plays often have only one act and one scene.

playwright   The author of a play.

plot   The sequence of actions and events in fiction or drama. A traditional plot has at least three parts: the *rising action,* leading up to a turning point that affects the main character; the *climax,* the turning point or moment of greatest intensity or interest; and the *falling action,* leading away from the conflict, or resolving it.

poetry   Language selected and arranged in order to say something in a compressed or nonliteral way. Modern poetry may or may not use many of the traditional poetic techniques that include *meter, rhyme, alliteration, figurative language, symbolism,* and *specific verse forms.*

point of view   The perspective from which a writer tells a story. *First-person* narrators tell the story from their own point of view, using pronouns like *I* or *me. Third-person* narrators, using pronouns like *he, she,* or *them,* may be *omniscient* (knowing everything about all characters), or *limited* (taking the point of view of one character). [See also *narration.*]

propaganda   Information or ideas that may or may not be true, but are spread as though they are true, in order to persuade people to do or believe something.

prose   The ordinary form of written and spoken language used to create fiction, nonfiction, and most drama.

protagonist   The main character of a literary work. [See also *character* and *characterization.*]

R

refrain   A line or group of lines that is repeated, usually at the end of each verse, in a poem or a song.

repetition   The use of the same formal element more than once in a literary work, for emphasis or in order to achieve another desired effect.

resolution   The "falling action" in fiction or drama,

including all of the developments that follow the climax and show that the story's conflict is over. [See also *plot*.]

rhyme scheme A repeated pattern of similar sounds, usually found at the ends of lines of poetry or poetic drama.

rhythm In poetry, the measured recurrence of accented and unaccented syllables in a particular pattern. [See also *meter*.]

S

scene The time, place, and circumstances of a play or a story. In a play, a scene is a section of an act. [See also *play*.]

science fiction Fantasy literature set in an imaginary future, with details and situations that are designed to seem scientifically possible.

setting The time and place of a work of literature.

short story Narrative prose fiction that is shorter and has a less complicated plot than a novel. A short story contains narration, at least one setting, at least one character, and usually some dialogue.

simile Figurative language that compares two unlike things, introduced by the words "like" or "as." [See also *figurative language*.]

soliloquy In a play, a short speech spoken by a single character when he or she is alone on the stage. A soliloquy usually expresses the character's innermost thoughts and feelings, when he or she thinks no other characters can hear.

sonnet A poem written in one stanza, using fourteen lines of iambic pentameter. [See also *meter*.]

speaker In poetry, the individual whose voice seems to be speaking the lines. [See also *narration*, *voice*.]

stage directions The directions, written by the playwright, to tell the director, actors, and theater technicians how a play should be dramatized. Stage directions may specify such things as how the setting should appear in each scene, how the actors should deliver their lines, when the stage curtain should rise and fall, how stage lights should be used, where on the stage the actors should be during the action, and when sound effects should be used.

stanza A group of lines in poetry set apart by blank lines before and after the group; a poetic verse.

style The distinctive way in which an author composes a

work of literature in written or spoken language.

suspense An effect created by authors of various types of fiction and drama, especially adventure and mystery plots, to heighten interest in the story.

symbol An image, person, place, or thing that is used to express the idea of something else.

T

tall tale A kind of folk tale, or legend, that exaggerates the characteristics of its hero or heroine.

theme The main idea or underlying subject of a work of literature.

tone The attitude that a work of literature expresses to the reader through its style.

tragedy In classical drama, a tragedy depicts a noble hero or heroine who makes a mistake of judgment that has disastrous consequences.

V

verse A stanza in a poem. Also, a synonym for poetry as a genre. [See also *stanza*.]

voice The narrator or the person who relates the action of a piece of literature. [See also *speaker*.]

ACKNOWLEDGMENTS

Grateful acknowledgment is made for permission to reprint the following copyrighted material.

"The Naming of Names" by Ray Bradbury, copyright 1949 by Ray Bradbury, is reprinted by permission of Don Congdon Associates, Inc.

"Paradise Lost" by Elizabeth Vitton from the December 1990 issue of *3-2-1 Contact* Magazine, copyright © 1990, Children's Television Workshop (New York, NY). All rights reserved.

"Harrison Bergeron" by Kurt Vonnegut, Jr., from *Welcome to the Monkey House* by Kurt Vonnegut, Jr. Copyright © 1961 by Kurt Vonnegut, Jr. Used by permission of Delacorte Press/Seymour Lawrence, a division of Bantam Doubleday Dell Publishing Group, Inc.

"Orbiter 5 Shows How Earth Looks from the Moon" by May Swenson is reprinted by permission of Macmillan Publishing Company from *The Complete Poems to Solve* by May Swenson. Copyright © 1993 by The Literary Estate of May Swenson.

"If I Forget Thee, Oh Earth . . . " by Arthur C. Clarke, copyright 1953 by Arthur C. Clarke, is reprinted from *Tales from Planet Earth* by permission of Scott Meredith Literary Agency.

"Homecoming" by Stephen David is reprinted from *Science Fiction Stories* by permission.

"So, You Want To Be an Astronaut" by Michael Ryan. Reprinted by permission of the author and the author's agents, Scovil Chichak Galen Literary Agency, Inc., 381 Park Avenue South, New York, New York 10016. Reprinted with permission from *Parade,* copyright © 1993.

"User Friendly" by T. Ernesto Bethancourt, copyright © 1989 by T. Ernesto Bethancourt from *Connections: Short Stories* by Donald R. Gallo, Editor. Used by permission of Delacorte Press, a division of Bantam Doubleday Dell Publishing Group, Inc.

"Where the Rainbow Ends" by Richard Rive is reprinted from *Poems from Black Africa*, edited by Langston Hughes, copyright ©1963 by Langston Hughes.

ILLUSTRATION

32 Map by John Rumery; 62-77 Eve Olitsky.

PHOTOGRAPHY

4 *l, r* Julie Bidwell/©D.C. Heath; 5 NASA; 6 Sarah Putnam/©D.C. Heath; 8–9 NASA; 10 *t* Richard Haynes/©D.C. Heath; *b* Jim Whitmer/Stock Boston; 11 *t, c* Sarah Putnam/©D.C. Heath; *b* John Owens/©D.C. Heath; 12–28 William Lesch/Swanstock; 29 *l* AP/Wide World Photos; *r* William Lesch/Swanstock; 30–31 Kathleen Norris Cook; 32 Thomas L. Kelly; 32–33 *background* Hans Silvester/Rapho; 33 Stephen Dalton/Animals Animals/Earth Scenes; 34 Frans Lanting/Minden Pictures; 35 *t* Gary Braasch; *b* Raymond A. Mendez/Animals Animals/ Earth Scenes; 36 *l* Frans Lanting/Minden Pictures; *r* Michael Fogden/Animals Animals/Earth Scenes; 37 Frans Lanting/Minden Pictures; 38 *t* Frans Lanting/Minden Pictures; *b* E.R. Degginger/Animals Animals/Earth Scenes; 39 *t* Michael Fogden/Animals Animals/Earth Scenes; *b* Photo by Jeff Kelly; 40, 45, 49 Courtesy Sperone Westwater, New York; 51 UPI/Bettmann Archive; 52–53 NASA; 53 *b* Courtesy of Literary Estate of Mary Swenson; 54–55, 58, 60, 61 NASA; 78–79, 82, 83 Courtesy of Saff Tech Arts; 84–99 Courtesy of International Business Machines Corporation; 99 *inset* Photo by Tom Tondee; 100–101 Frank Siteman/Tony Stone Images; 103 Nancy Sheehan; 106 Jerry Berndt/Stock Boston; 107 Arthur Tilley/FPG International; 108 Ken O'Donoghue/©D.C. Heath; 112 Sarah Putnam/©D.C. Heath; 113 Jon Nickson/©D.C. Heath; 114 Rhoda Sidney/Stock Boston; 115 Edward Koren.
Back cover *t* Julie Bidwell/©D.C. Heath; *c, b* Sarah Putnam/©D.C. Heath.

Full Pronunciation Key for Footnoted Words

(Each pronunciation and definition is adapted from *Scott, Foresman Advanced Dictionary* by E.L. Thorndike and Clarence L. Barnhart.)

The pronunciation of each footnoted word is shown just after the word, in this way: **abbreviate** [ə brē′ vē āt]. The letters and signs used are pronounced as in the words below. The mark ′ is placed after a syllable with primary or heavy accent, as in the example above. The mark ′ after a syllable shows a secondary or lighter accent, as in **abbreviation** [ə brē′ vē ā′ shən].

Some words, taken from foreign languages, are spoken with sounds that do not otherwise occur in English. Symbols for these sounds are given in the key as "foreign sounds."

a	hat, cap	j	jam, enjoy	u	cup, butter	**foreign sounds**
ā	age, face	k	kind, seek	ù	full, put	
ä	father, far	l	land, coal	ü	rule, move	Y as in French *du*.
		m	me, am	v	very, save	Pronounce (ē) with
b	bad, rob	n	no, in	w	will, woman	the lips rounded as
ch	child, much	ng	long, bring	y	young, yet	for (ü).
d	did, red			z	zero, breeze	
		o	hot, rock	zh	measure, seizure	à as in French *ami*.
e	let, best	ō	open, go			Pronounce (ä) with
ē	equal, be	ô	order, all	ə represents:		the lips spread and
ėr	term, learn	oi	oil, voice		a in about	held tense.
		ou	house, out		e in taken	
f	fat, if				i in pencil	œ as in French *peu*.
g	go, bag	p	paper, cup		o in lemon	Pronounce (ā) with the
h	he, how	r	run, try		u in circus	lips rounded as for (ō).
		s	say, yes			
i	it, pin	sh	she, rush			N as in French *bon*.
ī	ice, five	t	tell, it			The N is not pro-
		th	thin, both			nounced, but shows
		ᴛʜ	then, smooth			that the vowel before
						it is nasal.

H as in German *ach*. Pronounce (k) without closing the breath passage.